The Hyde Collection Catalogue

Text by
James K. Kettlewell

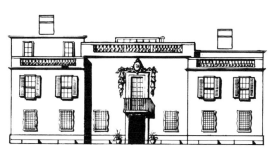

Glens Falls • New York • 1981

Dedicated to the Memory of

Louis Fiske Hyde and Charlotte Pruyn Hyde

Support for the research and publication of this catalogue
was provided by the following:
National Endowment for the Arts
New York State Council on the Arts
The Chase Manhattan Bank, N.A.
Finch, Pruyn and Company, Inc.
Gannett Foundation
The Glens Falls Foundation
Kamyr, Inc.
E. Yale Clarke, Memorial
David deBlasiis, Memorial
Michael A. Sinto, Memorial
Mr. & Mrs. Lyman A. Beeman, Sr.
Dr. & Mrs. Richard G. Day, Jr.

This catalogue was produced by
The Hyde Collection, Glens Falls, New York

Cover:
Joseph Mallard William Turner, *Grand Canal, Venice,* c. 1840,
watercolor, pastel, and gouache on paper, 1971.51

Contents

Acknowledgements

vii

Introduction

ix

Notes to the Catalogue

xiii

Index of Artists

xv

Catalogue of the Collection

1-235

Acknowledgements

While we are responsible for most of the research and conclusions presented here, three other art historians were extensively involved in the project. Kathleen Giles Arthur provided the primary research for the Italian section. This was revised and brought up to date by Eleanor M. Hight, who also made many contributions to the American section. Jane Rehl provided the research and most of the conclusions for the later French works of art. During the many years in which this catalogue was in preparation helpful observations were kindly given by Mojmír Frinta, Creighton Gilbert, Julius Held, Meredith Lillich, Ronald Lightbown, Otto Naumann, Carlo Pedretti, Seymour Slive, Wolfgang Stechow, Arthur Wheelock, and Andrew McLaren Young. Penny Jolly, Jane Rehl, Cecilia Esposito, and Frederick J. Fisher meticulously reviewed the content and writing of the text; their observations have been included throughout in too many instances to be cited. For review of the introductory material we are indebted to Barbara Hancock and Steven Van Slooten.

Important information about the condition and technical history of the works of art was provided in the last ten years by art conservators Morton Bradley, Carol Christensen, Gerald Hoepfner, Caroline and Sheldon Keck, Noël Kunz, Mary Kay Porter, John Washeba, William Young, and Joyce Zucker.

Patricia Musser thoroughly edited and prepared the text for publication. Special thanks must go to Cathy Kimball who proof-read and typed the final version.

To assure the best possible reproductions for this publication almost all of the works of art illustrated were photographed and the negatives printed by fine arts photographer Joseph Levy.

James K. Kettlewell
Curator

Library, Hyde House

Dining Room, Hyde House

Introduction

A bronze plaque, dated 1952, installed in the outer vestibule of the front entrance of Hyde House, reads: "The Hyde Collection, to the Memory of Samuel Pruyn and Eliza Baldwin Pruyn." At that time Charlotte Pruyn Hyde, then widowed for eighteen years, established a charitable and educational trust. Her home and its outstanding contents of fine and decorative arts were to become, at her death, a public art museum. It was dedicated ". . . to promote and cultivate the study and improvement of the fine arts for the education and benefit of the residents of Glens Falls and vicinity and the general public."

Charlotte Pruyn Hyde was born in Glens Falls, New York, in 1867, the eldest of three daughters of a leading industrialist family in the region. Her father, Samuel Pruyn, made his fortune in mining, lumbering, canal transportation, and paper manufacturing. In 1904, along with Jeremiah W. Finch, Samuel Pruyn founded the Finch, Pruyn and Company, Inc., on the banks of the Hudson River next to the Feeder Canal, a juncture of the Champlain Canal. Later to become solely owned by Pruyn, it formed the basis of the family wealth that ultimately enabled Charlotte and her husband Louis to assemble their important art collection.

After her primary education in Upstate New York, Charlotte Pruyn was sent to Boston in 1888 to attend a one year finishing school. During that year she met Louis Fiske Hyde, a Harvard Law School student who was living in the same boarding house. Hyde graduated from Harvard, with distinction, in 1890, and accepted a position with the Boston law firm of Messrs. Hyde, Dickinson, and Howe. Between 1898 and his retirement from law practice in 1906, he held several positions including one in the law department of the Boston Elevated Railway Company. In 1901, thirteen years after they met, Louis and Charlotte were married. They settled first in Hingham, Massachusetts where their only child, Mary Van Ness Hyde Whitney, was born in 1903.

The Hydes received a broad exposure to the arts early in their lives. Undoubtedly their tastes were most strongly influenced during their stay in Boston, at that time the cradle of the nation's cultural development. Louis's affiliation with Harvard had a lasting influence upon them both. One of his graduating classmates, Bernard Berenson, maintained an acquaintance with them over their years of art collecting. It can also be assumed that Harvard's art history professor, Charles Eliot Norton, who was a catalyst in the development of an impressive generation of art connoisseurs and collectors, must have directly or indirectly swayed the Hydes toward an avocation of art collecting. However, one of Boston's grandest ladies, Isabella

Stewart Gardner, had the most profound, albeit indirect, influence on Louis and Charlotte Hyde. Fenway Court, Mrs. Gardner's 1901 home designed in a Venetian Renaissance pastiche, was built to house her idiosyncratic art collection—an outstanding assemblage of old master works of art displayed among a large incongruous grouping of souvenirs. She was an innovator in America, creating a European—though historically incorrect—environment solely for collecting and exhibiting works of art. Mrs. Gardner's home was opened in 1903 and undoubtedly the Hydes must have been among the earliest of her enthusiastic visitors.

Charlotte Hyde's father, at age 86, persuaded Louis to accept the vice-presidency of the family paper company. After a year's sojourn in Europe, the Hydes moved to Glens Falls. In 1907 they settled in a temporary residence while planning their future home. The closeness of the Pruyn sisters is evidenced by their agreement to build homes next to each other on a single family complex located above and slightly east of Finch, Pruyn Paper Company. Charlotte's sister, Mary Eliza Hoopes was the first to establish her home on the property. In 1904 her husband Maurice, an engineer and president of the family company, commissioned architect Henry Forbes Bigelow, from the Boston firm of Bigelow and Wadsworth, to design their home in an English vernacular style. Bigelow was called upon again in 1910 to design the Finch, Pruyn headquarters-office building and a small ceramics studio. The studio was later to be expanded into a home for the youngest sister, Nellie Cunningham. In the same year Bigelow was also commissioned to design the largest and most prestigious of the three family dwellings, Hyde House. Built by the local contractor R. H. Rheinlander, it is spaciously centered between the two sisters' homes. The house is styled after Florentine Renaissance villa architecture—a reflection of the American Renaissance mentality of the day. The grounds of the family complex, connected by walkways and formal gardens, were designed by the Boston landscape architects, Brett and Hall. The lower grounds were gracefully terraced towards the Hudson River and included kitchen gardens, barns, and a carriage house.

Hyde House is a two-and-one-half story, stucco building with its most imposing facade facing south. The northern, street front entrance has a forbidding outer vestibule and door that opens into a small reception room leading directly into a brightly lighted interior, two story central court. Juxtaposed around and oriented towards the court are the living and gallery spaces modestly scaled but large enough to allow for a growing art collection.

The stucco walled, brick paved central court is naturally lighted through a skylight and arched clerestory windows on the south wall. It is conservatively appointed with decorative trelliswork and brick lined planting areas. A small rustic, stucco walled dining room leads from the court. Its ceiling is beamed and paneled with dark oiled ash. The floor is of hexagonal Mercer tiles. Across the court, opposite the dining room, is the spacious, barrel vaulted library that is dominated by a sixteenth century Italian hooded fireplace. The oiled gumwood paneled walls have recessed book shelves and the library floor is also laid with Mercer hexagonal tile. On the north side of the central court, and partially under the second floor picture gallery (now called the music room), is a vaulted loggia flanked by Knoxville marble columns. At the west end of the loggia is a guest bedroom and at right angles to it is the stairway leading to the second floor. There are five bedrooms in the house, all of which are understated in style. Two of the second story bedrooms have interior windows overlooking the central court. Crowning the second floor, on the north side of the house, is the picture gallery. It has French doors leading to wrought iron balconies on the inner central court and northern exterior. The gallery has a gable roofed ceiling with skylight and is braced with stained chestnut trusses held in place by carved gilt consoles. Without a doubt, Hyde House was designed to convey a warm European-like ambience suitable for collecting great works of art.

So impressed was Bigelow with Hyde House that in 1916 he built his private home along similar lines on Boston's prestigious Beacon Hill. Bigelow, too, was a collector, though on a more modest scale. Nevertheless, his interest in art ultimately led him to a trustee position with the Museum of Fine Arts, Boston.

The June 7, 1916 edition of *The American Architect* magazine devoted an entire issue to Bigelow's home. While it did not allude to Hyde House, it suggested the philosophical basis that motivated him and the Hydes to possess such unique homes:

Wherever . . . (one) turns his eye . . . (one) meets some bit that has associations of days abroad, or revives memories dear to the heart of every collector. Bit by bit this refining process goes on and it is only men of such temperamental qualities that can appreciate the comfort those artistic tendencies will secure with such a house and the large measure of satisfaction its possession affords.

Undoubtedly the Hyde's home and their predilection toward its decoration reflect a combination of early twentieth century influences. Mrs. Gardner's Fenway Court poses an obvious model, while the Hyde's motivations were far less flamboyant. Other influences too must be considered: Edith Wharton and Ogden Codman, Jr. were preaching in their books, *The Decoration of Houses* (1902), and *Italian Villas and Their Gardens* (1905), a more historical approach to private house design; and Elsie de Wolfe, who occasionally sold pieces of antique furniture to the Hydes and their family, was advising the nation's wealthy to throw off the bondage of their eclectic Victorian past and seek more cheerful and classic interior design.

Immediately after their house was constructed the Hydes eagerly engaged in its decoration. In 1913 they traveled to Paris, purchasing many pieces of European antique furniture. Their preference in furniture was primarily sixteenth century Italian and seventeenth and eighteenth century French. In keeping with the warm European ambience of their new home, the Hydes sought furnishings that were generally unpretentious yet evocative of the beautiful homes they had observed on their many sojourns abroad. Preferring simple understatement the Hydes decorated their home to complement their growing art collection. Windows were curtained with velvets, brocades, and toile muted in color to correspond to the natural building materials and the earthy greens and dulled tans of the painted walls. The bedrooms, severe in design, were decorated with French furniture and warm Aubusson rugs. In the picture gallery, French sixteenth century tapestries were hung on the walls and the room was furnished primarily with Italian late Renaissance pieces to complement many of the Renaissance works of art.

Their home was not as pretentious as the palatial mansions built for the Vanderbilts, Henry C. Frick, or J. P. Morgan. Indeed, their desire was not for a massive baronial shell in which to flaunt wealth, like the homes built for the industrial barons at Newport by McKim, Mead, and White. On the contrary, Hyde House represents a sincere reflection of ambition tempered with knowledge and made possible with financial comfort; not excess.

By 1920, having created a suitable ambience, the Hydes began the serious pursuit of acquiring works of art. Initially, on their own, they assembled a few cautiously chosen old masters. It was not long before they began seeking paid professional advice. In 1924 the Hydes purchased the small Botticelli *Annunciation* (number 23), undoubtedly with the aid of Bernard Berenson. In an article for the June, 1924 edition of *Art in America* Berenson wrote:

'Mere size is something' says Browning, and I never felt the significance of this unexpected declaration as much as I did in the presence of a tiny oblong panel belonging to Mr. Louis Hyde of Glens Falls, New York. For it lacks nothing that makes a masterpiece except size.

The Hydes' philosophical objectives in amassing their art collection were never recorded. Undoubtedly they collected primarily for the sheer enjoyment it gave them. They were eclectic in their tastes, acquiring late nineteenth century American pieces and French Impressionists along with important old masters. They were superbly sensitive to the quality, color, and scale of the works acquired. Most acquisitions are beautifully related to the architectural surroundings of their house. Certainly the Hydes' conservative financial means dictated their collecting habits, for they acquired smaller works of art, drawings, oil studies, and numerous male portraits. Nevertheless, they always predicated their decisions upon the merit of the work.

To avoid costly mistakes the Hydes took stock in the advice given them by William R. Valentiner, a noted connoisseur and art historian of the day. As early as 1922 he became aware of the Hydes through a mutual friend. But it was not until the early 1930s that he directly assisted them with purchases. Undoubtedly Valentiner's arbitration skills made it possible for the Hydes to purchase from the Soviet Union Rembrandt's *Portrait of Christ* (number 51). The internationally-renowned connoisseur was entertained at Hyde House to acquire some knowledge about the people and their ambitions as collectors. In 1931 he wrote them:

> Many thanks to you both for the delightful time I spent with you. It will always be a charming remembrance. I enjoyed so much the quiet and artistic atmosphere in your beautiful home, your lovely garden, and the fascinating visit to the paper mill.

The death of Louis Fiske Hyde in 1934, at age 68, greatly saddened his community. As one of Glens Falls' outstanding citizens he was duly mourned. The *Glens Falls Times* noted of his passing:

> He toiled and planned for the preservation of the beauty of our city and the creation of new beauty. He loved the trees and hated to have one cut down. He loved books and read the best of them. But it was not alone the beauty of love and nature and literature that he loved, but the beauty of truth and holiness, the beauty of human life and character.

In addition to his home and nascent art collection, Louis Hyde was vitally responsible for Glens Falls' architectural heritage. With his advice, Ralph Adams Cram was commissioned in 1928 to design the First Presbyterian Church, a stately Gothic edifice; and in 1930 Charles Adams Platt designed the outstanding Crandall Library.

During their years together, Louis and Charlotte led comfortable, patterned lives. In the winters, Charlotte stayed in their New York City East Side apartment while Louis remained in Glens Falls tending to his administrative responsibilities at the family company. Undoubtedly the cultural milieu of New York, including its art galleries and auction houses, was important in the development of Mrs. Hyde's art collecting tastes. In the summers, the Hydes traveled abroad together. They were enthusiastic tourists gaining new insights into their European cultural heritage and acquiring objects for their Glens Falls home.

Louis Hyde was an avid bibliophile and collector of rare books and manuscripts. He amassed a small but important book collection for himself and donated many rare books to the city library. He had a genuine interest in the history of the lower Adirondack region and, in his later life, wrote a scholarly book on Glens Falls that was published posthumously by his wife.

At the time of Hyde's death, one third of their art collection had been assembled. Charlotte continued to collect at the same pace after he passed away, carefully building a superb museum-quality collection. Moreover, the art world was becoming aware of their efforts and an occasional exhibition loan request was made for works in the collection. In 1938, four years after Louis's death, Mrs. Hyde, realizing the educational responsibility of the collection, hired her first curator, Otto Wittmann, Jr. fresh from Harvard's outstanding museum course taught by Paul J.

Sachs. Wittmann assisted and advised her on acquisitions, accumulated provenance data on her works of art, and most importantly, began to introduce The Hyde Collection to a limited public. He presented illustrated art history lectures in Mrs. Hyde's home, conducted tours of her collection, and established a sequence of temporary exhibitions in the Crandall Library, borrowing important paintings from New York City art dealers.

In 1941, Wittmann was drafted into the army. His replacement was Joseph Jeffers Dodge, who remained as Mrs. Hyde's Curator for twenty-one years. Dodge continued the activities begun by Wittmann but placed more emphasis on adult and children's fine arts classes taught by himself in the central court of Hyde House. More and more the collection was becoming better known. It was opened to the public on Sunday afternoons for guided tours by the Curator. During the years that Joseph Dodge remained with Mrs. Hyde, he aided her in purchasing more than one-third of the collection. Along with Valentiner and connoisseur Captain R. Langton Douglas, a long time friend of Mrs. Hyde, Dodge took an active role in guiding her to round out the collection. With his insistence, she purchased many of the later nineteenth and earlier twentieth century pieces.

Towards the end of her life, Charlotte Hyde became increasingly cognizant of the tremendous educational potential of her collection. Having always had a great love for talented young people — many of whom she gave financial assistance for their educations — it was only natural that she thought of her home and art collection as a future museum for the purpose of art education. Her 1952 trust provided the machinery and endowment for The Hyde Collection. She chose for her trustees family, friends, and local businessmen and instructed them through her trust not only to promote her collection but to allow it to grow, providing the small city of Glens Falls with a viable and outstanding art museum.

Charlotte Hyde, the friendly and unassuming citizen of Glens Falls died in her home in 1963. Her local newspaper not only wrote of her superb art collection but reminded its readers that she "...was a patron of music also, and a generous contributor to many other phases of the cultural life of the community. Her quiet philanthropy was known to few except those directly concerned."

This publication is dedicated to both Charlotte Pruyn and Louis Fiske Hyde. Through their avocation and love of the arts, they left to the public one of the finest small art collections in the nation. The intention herein is to document the Hyde's art collection as thoroughly as possible; to account not only for their great triumphs but also their occasional failures. The collection, still contained within its original setting, is a typical example of the transitory nature of art collecting. Indeed, today The Hyde Collection is as important to the history of art collecting as it is to the history of art.

Frederick J. Fisher
Director

Notes to the Catalogue

This review of the major works of art in The Hyde Collection is intended to be as complete as possible, equally useful to the scholar and to the person with a more general interest in art. At the end of each entry is the provenance (history) of the work, complete references to publications where it is mentioned or illustrated, and a record of the exhibitions in which it appeared. When not included, it is to be understood that this information was not available in the Hyde Archives or elsewhere.

The attribution of each work of art in the collection was carefully reconsidered. Changes in attribution are noted in the headings of each entry. Where attribution is an important question, it is discussed in the text. The authenticity and authorship of works of art was determined from the published and informally presented opinions of specialists; from laboratory analysis; from provenance, and documents; but the final decisions were our own, suggested in every case by a close comparison of the style and handwriting of works in the collection, with generally accepted works by the same artists elsewhere.

In each discussion, subject matter is analyzed, as is the place of the work of art in the artist's oeuvre and period. It is hoped that our conclusions will be wisely challenged and the errors and omissions in our information will be brought to our attention.

All works of art included were collected by Mr. and Mrs. Hyde together or, after Mr. Hyde's death in 1934, by Mrs. Hyde alone. Exceptions are four later gifts: George Bellows's *Portrait of Mary Brown Tyler,* Albert Bierstadt's *Yosemite Valley,* Dorothy Dehner's *Low Landscape Sideways,* and Elihu Vedder's *Marriage of the Daughter of the Vine.* Numerous gifts of lesser importance have been received in recent years, but it would seem appropriate to confine this first edition of the catalogue as much as possible to the original Hyde Collection. In the purchase of these works the Hydes proceeded largely on their own until around 1932, when they began to receive the advice of William R. Valentiner. Otto Wittmann, Jr. and Joseph Jeffers Dodge, two early curators of The Hyde Collection, also played an important part in the acquisition of works of art.

Measurements are given in the sequence of height first, then width, then depth where appropriate.

J. K. K.

Index of Artists

Artist	Work	Number	Page
Antwerp Mannerist School, *Adoration of the Kings,* **32**			70
Beham, Bartel, *Portrait of Philipp von der Pfalz, Bishop of Freising,* **33**			72
Bellows, George Wesley, *Portrait of Mary Brown Tyler,* **110**			230
Bierstadt, Albert, *Yosemite Valley,* **90**			190
Bol, Hans, *Valley of the Meuse with Apollo and Daphne,* **40**			86
Botticelli, Sandro, *Annunciation,* **23**			46
Boucher, François, *Vertumnus and Pomona,* **64**			138
Bruyn, Bartel, *Portrait of a Young Woman,* **34**			74
Caffiéri, Jean-Jacques, *Study for a River God,* **65**			140
Cézanne, Paul, *Trees,* **83**			176
Claude Lorrain, *Parnassus,* **56**			122
Colyer, Edwaert, *Vanitas Still Life,* **54**			118
Corneille de Lyon ?, *Portrait of the Count d'Angoulême,* **35**			76
Courbet, Gustave, *Waterfall Near Ornans,* **79**			168
Cozzarelli, Giacomo ?, *Madonna and Child,* **25**			52
Degas, Hilaire Germain Edgar, *Dancer with Red Stockings,* **75**			160
Degas, Hilaire Germain Edgar, *Dancer Tying Her Scarf,* **77**			164
Degas, Hilaire Germain Edgar, *Draught Horse,* **76**			162
Degas, Hilaire Germain Edgar, *Mlle. Marguerite Degas (Mme. Fevre),* **74**			158
Dehner, Dorothy, *Low Landscape Sideways,* **112**			234
Despiau, Charles, *Mask of Madame Despiau ?,* **89**			188
Desiderio da Settignano, after, *The Christ Child,* **14**			28
Duveneck, Frank, *Munich Professor,* **100**			210
Eakins, Thomas, *In the Studio — Girl and Dog,* **91**			192
Eakins, Thomas, *Portrait of Henry O. Tanner,* **92**			194
English, c. 1350, alabaster sculpture, *St. Augustine,* **8**			16
Flemish, c. 1600, tapestry, *Allegory of Spring with Flora, Vertumnus, and Pomona,* **41**			88
Fragonard, Jean-Honoré, *Le Fauçon,* **66**			142
French, c. 1325, stained glass, *Christ's Entry into Jerusalem,* **3**			6
French, early sixteenth century, tapestry, *Millefleurs,* **29**			60
French ?, c. 1475-1500, painting, *St. Peter Enthroned,* **21**			42
French school, c. 1820, painting, *Portrait of a Young Girl,* **68**			146
French, c. 1195, stained glass, *Presentation of the Christ Child in the Temple,* **2**			4
French, c. 1500, tapestry, *Triumph of Eternity,* **28**			58
French, c. 1500, tapestry, *Triumph of Love,* **27**			56
German or French, c. 1485, wood sculpture, *The Virgin Mary,* **19**			38
German, c. 1500, wood sculpture, *Virgin Mary,* **20**			40
Greco, El, *Portrait of St. James the Less,* **42**			90
Greek, c. 350 B.C., marble sculpture, *Mourning Woman,* **1**			2
Guardi, Francesco or Giacomo ?, *Venice, the Arsenal,* **63**			136
Hals, Frans, Circle of, so-called *Portrait of the Artist's Son,* **45**			96
Hassam, Childe, *Geraniums,* **102**			214
Hassam, Childe, *Girl in Pink/In the Garden,* **103**			216
Homer, Winslow, *A Good One, Adirondacks,* **98**			206
Homer, Winslow, *Forebodings,* **97**			204
Homer, Winslow, *St. John's River, Florida,* **99**			208
Huntington, Anna Hyatt, *Mountain Lion,* **109**			228
Ingres, Jean-Auguste-Dominique, *Study for the Head of Victory,* **70**			150
Ingres, Jean-Auguste-Dominique, *Paolo and Francesca,* **72**			154
Ingres, Jean-Auguste-Dominique, *Study for the Odyssey,* **71**			152
Italian, c. 1350, painting, *Equestrian Crucifixion,* **6**			12
Italian, c. 1500, marble, *Fountain,* **26**			54
Kuniyoshi, Yasuo, *A Friend,* **111**			232

Leonardo da Vinci, *Cartoon for the Mona Lisa*, **30**	62
Mantegna, Andrea ?, *Madonna and Child*, **12**	24
Master of the Buckingham Palace Madonnas ?, *Sts. Nicholas, Lawrence, and John the Baptist*, **9**	18
Master of Città di Castello ?, *Crucifixion Triptych*, **4**	8
Matisse, Henri, *Two Draped Nudes*, **87**	184
Matisse, Henri, *Seated Nude*, **88**	186
Matteo di Giovanni di Bartolo, *The Dance of Salome*, **16**	32
Memling, Hans, School of, *Head of Christ*, **18**	36
Metcalf, Willard Leroy, *Zuni Indians*, **101**	212
Mieris, Frans van, The Elder, School of, *The Oyster Meal*, **55**	120
Molijn, Pieter de, *Landscape*, **47**	100
Murphy, J. Francis, *Landscape*, **106**	222
Neeffs, Pieter the Elder ?, *Interior of a Gothic Church*, **46**	98
Niccolò di ser Sozzo Tegliacci ?, *Angel*, **7**	14
Pannini, Giovanni Paolo, *Scene in the Roman Campagna*, **58**	126
Pellegrino di Mariano, *Assumption of the Virgin Mary*, **13**	26
Perugino, Pietro, School of, *Madonna with Two Saints*, **24**	50
Peto, John Frederick, *Still Life with Mug, Pipe, and Book*, **96**	202
Picasso, Pablo, *Boy Holding a Blue Vase*, **85**	180
Picasso, Pablo, *Four Figures*, **86**	182
Pissarro, Camille, *Sous-Bois*, **78**	166
Prud'hon, Pierre-Paul, *Charles-Hubert Millevoye*, **69**	148
Raphael Sanzio, *Portrait of a Young Man*, **31**	66
Rembrandt Harmenszoon van Rijn, *Portrait of Christ*, **51**	108
Rembrandt Harmenszoon van Rijn, *Portrait of the Artist's Mother*, **49**	104
Rembrandt Harmenszoon van Rijn, *Two Men Shaking Hands*, **50**	106
Renoir, Pierre-Auguste, *Coco*, **81**	172
Renoir, Pierre-Auguste, *Estelle in a Red Hat*, **80**	170
Robbia, Andrea della, *The Virgin Mary*, **17**	34
Robbia, Luca della, *Madonna with the Lilies*, **11**	22
Rossellino, Antonio, Follower of, *Madonna and Child with Angels*, **15**	30
Rubens, Peter Paul, *Head of a Negro*, **44**	94
Rubens, Peter Paul, *Man in Armor*, **43**	92
Ruisdael, Jacob van, *Landscape Near Castle Bentheim*, **52**	112
Ryder, Albert Pinkham, *Stag in the Forest of Arden*, **108**	226
Sano di Pietro, *Angel of the Annunciation*, **10**	20
Seurat, Georges, *Banks of the Seine Near Courbevoie*, **82**	174
Spanish, c. 1650, wood relief, *Adoration of the Christ Child*, **57**	124
Thayer, Abbott Handerson, *Mary: Portrait of the Artist's Daughter*, **107**	224
Tiepolo, Giambattista, *The Christ Child*, **61**	132
Tiepolo, Giambattista, *Madonna and Child with Saints and Bishops*, **59**	128
Tiepolo, Giambattista, *Madonna and Child with St. Catherine and the Infant St. John*, **60**	130
Tino di Camaino, *Mary as Queen of Heaven with the Christ Child*, **5**	10
Tintoretto (Jacopo Robusti), *The Discovery of the True Cross*, **37**	80
Tintoretto (Jacopo Robusti), *Portrait of the Doge Alvise Mocenigo*, **38**	82
Titian, School of, *Portrait of Doge Petrus Lando ?*, **36**	78
Turner, Joseph Mallard William, *Grand Canal, Venice*, **73**	156
Van Dyke, Anthony, *Portrait of Jan Woverius*, **48**	102
Van Gogh, Vincent, *Corner of a Field*, **84**	178
Vedder, Elihu, *Girl Reading in XVth Century Costume*, **94**	198
Vedder, Elihu, *Marriage of the Daughter of the Vine*, **95**	200
Vedder, Elihu, *Palo. Ruins of an Old Castle*, **93**	196
Vermeer, Jan, Style of, *Girl with Blue Bow*, **53**	114
Veronese, Paolo, *Rebecca at the Well*, **39**	84
Wedgwood, Josiah and John Flaxman, *Portrait of Carl von Linnaeus*, **67**	144
Whistler, James Abbott McNeill ?, *Tatting*, **104**	218
Whistler, James Abbott McNeill, *The Sea, Pourville, No. 1*, **105**	220
Wolgemut, Michael and Wilhelm Pleydenwurff, *The Nuremberg Chronicle*, **22**	44
Zuccarelli, Francesco, *Italian Landscape*, **62**	134

The Hyde Collection Catalogue

1. Greek

Attic

Mourning Woman, c. 350 B.C.

Pentelic marble. 83.8 x 68 x 34.3 cm. (33 x 26-3/4 x 13-1/2″) 1971.89

This sculpture of a mourning woman was probably once joined to a larger slab shaped to resemble a temple, or *naiskos,* with pilasters at the side carrying a pedimented gable above.[1] Carved in very high relief, the figure was attached only by a narrow vertical band on the side away from the viewer. The figure would have turned slightly outward at a thirty-degree angle. A small section of the lower right cheek and lips survives, indicating that the head would have been bent down and slightly to the left. The legs are crossed. The outer garment is a himation which would have once covered the head. Beneath the himation the woman wears a belted chiton. Three drill holes indicate that a bronze belt would have been attached to the marble. The left hand on the lap holds the folds of the garment, while the missing right hand probably grasped the hood of the himation, a traditional gesture of mourning.

Consistent with Attic funerary art, the woman portrayed would have been a generalized type, an allegory of mourning, rather than any specific person. Women played an important part in funerary rites by preparing the body for burial, and it was their specific role to visibly and audibly mourn for the deceased.

The style of the carving is the anti-classical manner of the mid-fourth century, in which the surfaces and contours are broken into nervous rhythms and planes, consistent with the emotional expressiveness of Greek art of the period. This would be in contrast to the calmer, more harmonious, and more unified high classical style of the Parthenon sculpture of a century before.

1. Research by Eleanor M. Hight, Harvard University.

Provenance: Purchased from the Brummer Gallery, Inc., New York, 1941 (?). According to records in the possession of Mrs. Ella Brummer, Durham, N.C., it was acquired by Joseph Brummer from the Zoumboulakis-Roussos Gallery, Athens, January 1925.

Literature: S. Lane Faison, Jr., *Art Tours and Detours in New York State,* p. 110; fig. 182.

2. French Gothic

Lyons

Presentation of the Christ Child in the Temple, c. 1195

Stained glass. 69.7 x 58.4 cm. (24-7/16 x 23″) 1971.112

This stained glass belongs at the early phase of French Gothic art, reflecting well the characteristics of the period style: absence of mass and space, a degree of abstractness in forms, and an effect of decorative splendor. Although restoration has altered the original representation, it is, nonetheless, an important example of Medieval stained glass.

The *Presentation of the Christ Child in the Temple* depicts the first recorded instance in the New Testament of the substantiation of Christ as the Savior of mankind. The event is chronicled only in the Gospel of St. Luke, II, 21-40. In accord with Jewish religious law, Mary and Joseph brought Jesus to the temple in Jerusalem to be presented to God. However, events did not follow the traditional course. At the temple Simeon, a man with the Holy Spirit upon him, gathered the Holy Child in his arms and declared, "Lord, now lettest thou thy servant depart in peace, according to thy word; for mine eyes have seen the salvation, which thou has prepared before the face of all people" (Luke, II, 29-31). Earlier Simeon had been directed to the temple by the Holy Spirit and informed that "he should not see death before he had seen the Lord's Christ" (Luke, II, 29). Concurrently Anna, a prophetess, entered the temple and "gave thanks likewise unto the Lord, and spoke of him to all them who looked for redemption in Jerusalem" (Luke, II, 38). Thus these uncommon occurrences confirmed Jesus as "the Lord's Christ"; i.e., the Messiah, Savior of mankind.

In the window Anna appears on the right, distinctly identified by the attribute of the scroll in her left hand, but the figures at the altar constitute a problem. Nancy Kraus and others have identified many pieces of glass in the window as replacements.[1] The figure holding the Christ Child originally was the Virgin Mary, characteristic of Gothic arrangements of this subject. A restorer later misinterpreted her as Simeon in keeping with the Biblical text. However, in the typical Gothic treatment of this theme, Mary would not yet have presented the child to Simeon. The male figure on the left is more likely Simeon, as his arms are extended to receive the child. On the far left is Joseph, bringing two doves for the sacrifice as required by the rites of presentation.

A letter to Louis F. Hyde from Joseph Brummer, the dealer who sold the work, states "it belongs to the Lyons School."[2] Nancy Kraus and other scholars have supported this position. Kraus identifies the restorer of the glass as Émile Thibaud of Clermont who worked on a number of windows in Lyons Cathedral in the 1840's.

1. Everson Museum of Art, *Medieval Art in Upstate New York,* Syracuse, 1974, p. 18, no. 7, illustrated. Entry by Nancy Kraus.
2. Letter from Joseph Brummer, art dealer, New York, November 15, 1928.

Provenance: Charnoz Collection, Paris, early 1920's (according to Kraus); purchased from Brummer Gallery, Inc., New York, 1928.

Literature: Everson Museum of Art, *op. cit.*

Exhibitions: Everson Museum of Art, *Medieval Art in Upstate New York,* Syracuse, 1974.

3. French Gothic

Rouen

Christ's Entry into Jerusalem, c. 1325

Stained glass. 51 x 34.6 cm. (20-1/16 x 13-5/8″) 1971.114

One of the most common themes of Christian art is that of Christ's entry into Jerusalem. The importance of the subject lies in its emphatic demonstration that Christ was the Messiah whose coming was prophesied in the Old Testament: "Rejoice greatly, O daughter of Zion; shout, O daughter of Jerusalem: behold, thy King cometh unto thee: he is just, and having salvation; lowly, and riding upon an ass, and upon a colt the foal of an ass." (Zechariah, IX, 9). Moreover, his entry is described in all four gospels: Matthew XXI, Mark XI, Luke XIX, and John XII.

Because this theme was such a trenchant symbol, the arrangement remained unchanged for a thousand years of Christian art. The towered gates of Jerusalem are discernible on the right. Common to many depictions of this event is the figure in the tree to the right of Christ. This is intended to represent Zacchaeus the publican who, because he was of small stature, climbed a tree to see Jesus (Luke, XIX, 4).

Entering the city in this manner, Christ thus imitates the triumphal entry of a king and consciously presents himself to the people as the Messiah.

Dr. Meredith Lillich has demonstrated convincingly that the window came from Rouen, France, possibly even from the cathedral at Saint-Ouen.[1] While many of the pieces of glass have been restored, the work includes much that is authentic, including many fine passages of Gothic draftsmanship.

1. Everson Museum of Art, *Medieval Art in Upstate New York,* Syracuse, 1974, p. 24, no. 10, illustrated. Entry by Meredith Lillich.

Literature: *Ibid.*

Exhibitions: *Medieval Art in Upstate New York,* Everson Museum of Art, Syracuse, 1974.

4. Master of Città di Castello ?

Italian (Sienese), active 1325-50

Crucifixion Triptych, c. 1325

Tempera and gold leaf on wooden panel. 46 x 48.8 cm. (18-1/8 x 19-1/4″) 1971.5

In Italy during the fourteenth century the triptych became popular, not only for the functional fact that the picture surface could be closed to protect it, but also because when open, it resembled the cross section of a Gothic church with pointed vaults, a central nave, and flanking aisles.

The crucified Christ, accompanied by angels, the Virgin Mary, Mary Magdalen, and St. John, is depicted in the central panel. Each of the two wings of the triptych is divided into three registers. In the lower register of the left wing, a nun kneels before St. Benedict, suggesting that the painting may have originally been commissioned for a chapel in a convent. St. Dominic or St. Thomas Aquinas stands alone in the lower register of the right wing. Represented in the center register on the left wing is St. Dominic with St. Paul, who can be identified by his attribute, the sword. On the right wing in the middle zone stands St. John the Baptist with (probably) the Bishop St. Nicholas. The Annunciation is depicted in the top registers of the wings. On the right wing Mary is shown standing. The angel Gabriel is portrayed kneeling on the left.

The attribution given here is by Creighton Gilbert:

The little triptych is by a follower of Duccio known as the Master of Città di Castello. The figures of St. John and Mary are the ones that instantly identify this work as from the Duccio circle and nowhere else, if their qualities at the same time do suggest its late phase, showing awareness of Simone Martini. (Simone is most visible in the Angel of the Annunciation.) The Città di Castello Master is revealed by the unusually emphatic chiaroscuro and frontal figures, and you will find detailed comparisons of heads, etc. in the illustrations of Berenson, to name the most convenient source. The Annunciation composition is unusual, but is closely paralleled as to the poses in the little Blumenthal triptych in the Metropolitan Museum. The Master is generally thought to have been at work up to 1325, on the basis of known works, and this would be not much earlier and possibly even a bit later. . . . It is interesting that the work was ordered by a Dominican nun whose personal patron was St. Benedict.[1]

1. Letter in the Hyde Archives from Creighton Gilbert, July 5, 1977.

Literature: Everson Museum of Art, *Medieval Art in Upstate New York,* Syracuse, 1974, p. 66, no. 43, illustrated. Entry by Mojmír Frinta.

Exhibitions: *Medieval Art in Upstate New York,* Everson Museum of Art, Syracuse, 1974.

5. Tino di Camaino

Italian, 1285?-1337

Mary as Queen of Heaven with the Christ Child, c. 1330

Marble. 48.9 x 37.8 x 4.7 cm. (19-1/4 x 14-7/8 x 1-7/8″) 1971.101

Mary, adorned with a crown as the Queen of Heaven, sits with the infant Jesus on her lap. Jesus grasps a goldfinch, symbol of his coming suffering and final resurrection. Mary herself holds grapes, a Eucharistic symbol of the blood that Christ will shed. The sculpture is an example of Tino's late manner and was executed while he was in the employ of the King of Naples, Robert d'Anjou.

The solid, classical face of Mary survives from the classicizing style of Nicola Pisano. The earliest record of Tino is as an assistant to Giovanni Pisano, Nicola's son, at the Cathedral of Siena.

Sienese precedents exist for other aspects of Tino's style. The warm exchange between mother and child was a common motif of Tino's close friend, the painter Pietro Lorenzetti, while the soft modeling of the forms suggests the influence of Pietro's brother Ambrogio. The graceful curves of the drapery folds are similar to Simone Martini's artistic conventions which affected Tino's later style.

A close replica of this sculpture is in the Victoria and Albert Museum in London. The Hyde relief is also similar in scale and format to Tino's *Votive Relief of Queen Sanzia* (National Gallery of Art, Washington, D.C.). The Hyde work appears to be the latest of the three because of the greater depth in the carving of the drapery and the similarities to the *Madonna and Child* from the tomb of Giovanni of Durazzo (San Domenico, Naples), which dates from the last two years of Tino di Camaino's life.

It is possible that this relief may have been a part of a larger altarpiece which has since been dispersed. However, the subject matter and the fine finish of the surface suggest that it may also have been an isolated votive image.

Provenance: Purchased from a private collection in Rome through the arrangement of W. R. Valentiner, 1938.

Literature: S. Lane Faison, Jr., *Art Tours and Detours in New York State,* New York, 1964, p. 110, fig. 183. Everson Museum of Art, *Medieval Art in Upstate New York,* Syracuse, 1974, pp. 42-44, no. 24, illustrated. Entry by Barbara Sacks.

Exhibitions: New York State Pavilion, World's Fair, New York, 1964, 1965; *Medieval Art in Upstate New York,* Everson Museum of Art, Syracuse, 1974.

6. Italian

(Umbrian?)

Equestrian Crucifixion, c. 1350

Tempera and gold leaf on wooden panel. 59 x 28 cm. (23-1/2 x 11") 1971.4

Mojmír Frinta states that this subject belongs to a Crucifixion type known as the "Equestrian Crucifixion" because some of the soldiers are on horseback. On the left can be seen the traditional group of the fainting Virgin supported by three women, while on the right St. John looks on with concern. It is interesting to note that two of the mounted officers have unusual hexagonal halos.[1]

Often represented in Gothic art is the pelican nesting at the top of the cross. According to legend, the pelican demonstrates more love for its offspring than any other living creature to the extent that it will sacrifice its own blood to nourish its young. Thus the pelican came to symbolize Christ's sacrifice on the cross, his eternal love for all mankind, and the sacrament of the Eucharist.

The gold that appears in the sky represents the light of God, removing the scene from a historical context. However, the emotional figures indicate the artist is moving away from earlier Gothic conventions toward a more natural drama. Such emotional expression is a characteristic innovation of the art of early fourteenth century Italy.

The painting has been extensively reworked by a modern hand, but it appears to belong to the tradition of the Sienese painters Ambrogio and Pietro Lorenzetti. In the punch patterns that decorate the borders of the Hyde panel, Frinta identifies a small trefoil punch which was originally used by Ambrogio and, more rarely by Pietro.[2] A similar Crucifixion by Ambrogio Lorenzetti is in the Fogg Art Museum, Cambridge, Massachusetts. Both the Hyde and the Fogg panels are comparable in size and shape, and both depict the soldiers on horseback behind the fainting Virgin. In the Fogg panel four mourning angels, rather than two, fly in the air beside the cross.

Frinta suggests a possible attribution of this painting to Guido Palmerucci of Gubbio, both on stylistic grounds and for the fact that Guido appears to have inherited punches from the Lorenzetti studio.[3]

1. Everson Museum of Art, *Medieval Art in Upstate New York,* Syracuse, 1974, p. 67, no. 44, illustrated. Entry by Mojmír Frinta.
2. *Ibid.*
3. *Ibid.*

Literature: Ibid.

Exhibitions: Medieval Art in Upstate New York, Everson Museum of Art, Syracuse, 1974.

7. Niccolò di ser Sozzo Tegliacci ?

Italian (Sienese), d. 1363
(Formerly School of Pietro Lorenzetti.)

Angel, c. 1350

Tempera and gold leaf on wooden panel. 32.7 x 24.7 cm. (12-3/4 x 9-3/4") 1971.27

From a large altarpiece of many panels, this angel would have appeared in one of the pinnacles above an enthroned Virgin Mary. Although sometimes considered to be the angel Gabriel from an Annunciation, the quiescence of the crossed-arm pose and the intent downward glance are not consistent with an Annunciation subject. A pose and expression similar to this occur in the angels accompanying a Pietro Lorenzetti *Madonna Enthroned* (Philadelphia Museum of Art, Johnson Collection).

Although once attributed to P. Lorenzetti or his school by Langton Douglas,[1] Creighton Gilbert has recently suggested that the painting is by Tegliacci, a noted miniaturist: "The angel 1971.27 is by Niccolò di ser Sozzo Tegliacci. It is also quite close to Lippo Vanni, a contemporary of his 1340-60. The main work of Niccolò, his altarpiece in collaboration with Luca di Tomme, shows this type of angel nicely."[2]

1. R. Langton Douglas, "Photographic Evidence," *Burlington Magazine,* LX, June 1932, p. 282, pl. 1A.
2. Letter from Creighton Gilbert, July 5, 1977.

Provenance: From the collections of Sir Archibald Buchan-Hepburn, Bt.; Captain R. Langton Douglas; the Right Honorable Godfrey Locker-Lampson; purchased from Parke-Bernet Galleries, Inc., New York, 1947.

Literature: Langton Douglas, *op. cit.;* Langton Douglas, *A Few Pictures Collected by Godfrey Locker-Lampson,* London [1937], p. 28, illustrated p. 29; Everson Museum of Art, *Medieval Art in Upstate New York,* Syracuse, 1974, p. 68, no. 45, illustrated. Entry by Mojmír Frinta.

Exhibitions: Winter exhibition, Burlington Fine Arts Club, London, 1930-31, no. 64; *The Commonwealth of Painting,* Addison Gallery of American Art, Andover, Mass., 1946, no. 1; *Medieval Art in Upstate New York,* Everson Museum of Art, Syracuse, 1974, no. 45.

8. English

St. Augustine, c. 1350

Alabaster. 50.5 x 34.9 x 23.5 cm. (19-7/8 x 13-3/4 x 9-1/4″) 1971.87

From the time that alabaster was first carved in England early in the fourteenth century, the style evolved so little that sculptures cannot be exactly dated, though all may be classified as Gothic.

That it represents St. Augustine is indicated by the identifying emblem of a heart, which appears at the base of the enthroned Trinity held in the figure's right hand. The Trinity itself is a reference to Augustine's great work on the theology of the Holy Trinity, which involved thirty years and comprised fifteen books. Augustine, Bishop of Hippo in Northern Africa, from 396 to his death in 430, is always represented with a bishop's robe and mitre. The book he holds may also be an attribute, a reference to St. Augus-

tine's famous conversion to Christianity when he heard a voice saying, "take up and read." (Described in his *Confessions.)*[1]

It is probable that the sculpture would have served as a devotional image somewhere within the precincts of an English cathedral. Many such sculptures were dispersed during the Cromwellian Revolution in the middle of the seventeenth century. The alabaster material almost certainly indicates an English source. Early in the fourteenth century alabaster was mined in Nottinghamshire and Derbyshire, and around 1330 became the favorite material for funerary effigies, production concentrating in London, Chellaston, Nottingham, and York.

1. St. Augustine, *The Basic Writings of St. Augustine,* New York, 1948, I, p. 126.

Provenance: Purchased from Karl Freund, 1919.

9. Master of the Buckingham Palace Madonnas ?

Italian (Florentine), active mid-fifteenth century
(Formerly Domenico di Michelino.)

Sts. Nicholas, Lawrence, and John the Baptist, c. 1450

Tempera and gold leaf on wooden panel. 76.2 x 47 cm. (30 x 18-1/2") 1971.29

Presumably the left panel of a triptych, this painting portrays three easily recognizable figures. St. Nicholas of Bari can be identified by his mitre and by the purse of gold which, according to legend, he secretly gave to penniless girls. In the center St. Lawrence stands upon the instrument of his martyrdom, a grid on which he was roasted to death. St. John the Baptist on the right can always be identified by his fur clothing. The right wing of this altarpiece is in the Jarves Collection (Yale University Art Gallery, New Haven). Attributed to the Master of the Buckingham Palace Madonnas by Charles Seymour, Jr.,[1] it includes Sts. Zenobius, Francis, and Anthony of Padua. It is reasonably certain that an enthroned Madonna would have been the subject of the central panel (now lost). A corner of her robe appears in the lower right of the Hyde painting. According to R. Langton Douglas, from whom the painting was purchased in 1940, the central panel was originally in the monastery of San Salvi in Florence.

When the painting was purchased Langton Douglas noted in a letter to Mrs. Hyde that he had originally attributed it to Andrea di Giusto.[2] He added that he now followed Berenson's attribution of the panel at Yale to Domenico di Michelino.[3]

The style of the work, conservative for its time, is derived from the style of the Florentine master Fra Angelico. The technique, tempera on gold on a gesso covered wooden panel, continues the traditional medieval medium for sacred art.

---

1. Charles Seymour, Jr., *Early Italian Paintings in the Yale University Art Gallery,* New Haven, 1970, p. 159.
2. In J. A. Crowe and G. B. Cavalcaselle, *A History of Painting in Italy,* ed. Langton Douglas, New York, 1911, IV, p. 64, note 2.
3. Bernard Berenson, *Italian Painters of the Renaissance, Florentine School,* London, 1963, I, p. 60.

Provenance: F. E. Sidney Collection, Richmond and Hampstead, England; purchased from Langton Douglas, 1940.

Literature: *Burlington House Exhibition Catalogue,* London, 1903, no. 43?; J. A. Crowe and G. B. Cavalcaselle, *op. cit.;* Osvald Siren, *A Descriptive Catalogue of the Pictures in the Jarves Collection belonging to Yale University,* New Haven, London, Oxford, 1916, p. 80.

10. Sano di Pietro

Italian (Sienese), 1406-1481

Angel of the Annunciation (Gabriel), c. 1450

Tempera on wooden panel. 36.8 x 34.3 cm. (14-1/2 x 13-1/2") 1971.44

This portrayal of the angel Gabriel at the Annunciation once must have included a separate panel to the right with the Virgin Mary. In every particular, the traditional Sienese format for this sacred subject was followed by the artist. The angel holds, for example, an olive branch in his left hand, a reference to the olive leaf born to Noah by the dove as a sign that the flood would subside. Thus, the olive branch became a symbol of the salvation that was brought to mankind with the advent of Christ. It was also traditional to place the angel and Mary beneath separate arches. In this instance the arch surrounding Mary would have been the frame of a separate panel, long since disappeared.

The subject of the Annunciation appears only in the Gospel of St. Luke, I, 26-38. According to this passage Gabriel descends to inform Mary, a virgin, that "thou shalt conceive in thy womb, and bring forth a son, and shall call his name Jesus."

The painting is generally accepted to be by Sano di Pietro. In 1933 W. R. Valentiner originally certified the work to be from Sano's hand. Later, in 1965, this attribution received interesting, though not certain, support in Mojmír Frinta's observation that the ivy leaf punch marks in the angel's halo also appear in the halos in Sano di Pietro's *Four Saints* (Pinacoteca Gallery, Siena).[1] The same punch mark appears in the halo of Sano's *Madonna and Child,* also in Siena.

1. Mojmír Frinta, "An Investigation of the Punched Decoration of Medieval Italian and Non-Italian Panel Paintings," *Art Bulletin,* XLVII, June 1965, p. 262, illustrations, p. 259. Frinta mistakenly claims that The Hyde Collection had attributed the work to Giovanni di Paolo.

Provenance: Once owned by German art historian Dr. Rudolph Grosse, Berlin; purchased from Dr. S. F. Aram, New York, 1933.

Literature: The Detroit Institute of Arts, *Catalogue of the Loan Exhibition of Italian Paintings from the Fourteenth to the Sixteenth Century,* March 8-30, 1933, no. 58; Frinta, *op. cit.,* pp. 259 and 262.

11. Luca della Robbia

Italian (Florentine), 1400-1482

Madonna with the Lilies, c. 1450-60

Glazed terra cotta. 45.5 x 37 cm. (17-1/2 x 14-1/2″) 1971.99

Like many of Della Robbia's works, this sculpture probably once formed part of a small altarpiece in a chapel or in the side aisle of a church. The subject is unusual in iconographical history, having no apparent precedent. Because the Virgin Mary is seated on the ground, the arrangement may be derived from the theme of the *Madonna of Humility.* The unusual feature is the Christ Child reaching out and grasping a stalk of lilies. Symbolically the lily refers to the resurrection of the body that is to occur for all good Christians, the purpose of Christ's Incarnation.[1] In the context of the Hyde Della Robbia, the lily probably portends Christ's own Death and Resurrection. It may be that the pose of the seated Virgin Mary is an oblique allusion to the Virgin Mary of the *Pietà* where the dead Christ will lie across her lap.

The subject of the Hyde work must have been popular, because five versions of it from the Della Robbia workshop can be identified. While Allan Marquand doubted that this terra cotta was by Luca della Robbia himself, every subsequent scholar from Wilhelm Bode to John Pope-Hennessy[2] has enthusiastically defended it as an autograph work by the master. The different variations of this subject are often described as being Madonnas of the Rovezzano type because of the example still remaining in the Church of S. Andrea in Rovezzano, Italy. Slight differences distinguish the various terra cottas. The Hyde version would appear to be one of the finest in the group. It is almost like that at Rovezzano, but with small distinctions, such as the fact that at Rovezzano the Madonna's ear is completely uncovered. In a variation in the Museum of Fine Arts, Boston, the Madonna wears what appears to be a turban, sits on a clearly defined tasseled pillow, and the Christ Child wraps his hand completely around the lily's stem. In the Hyde version, and in the example in the Lichtenstein Collection, the pillow is treated unclearly, but in the latter, the turban headdress is still more definite than in the Boston example. These differences between the versions of the Rovezzano Madonna indicate that this composition was not reproduced by casting, a common practice later in the Della Robbia workshop, but rather that each version was individually modeled.

It is interesting to note that making large-scale sculptures in glazed terra cotta was an original idea of Luca della Robbia's. The technique, developed in the early 1440's, remained a carefully guarded secret of his workshop for the next seventy-five years. His glazing methods were derived from the techniques used in making the majolica pottery that had been introduced into Italy in the late Middle Ages. Della Robbia's terra cotta sculptures were less expensive than other sculpture media and were impervious to the weather. At the same time, the gleaming surfaces and brilliant hues were immensely appealing to the eye. The essential creamy white hue of the principal figures was devised to resemble the color of marble. The blue background, which could both represent the blue sky and symbolically, a sacred heavenly environment, was the traditional color against which sculpture had been set off dating back to the temples of the Greeks.

1. One famous instance may be cited where the lily's association with resurrection is quite clear. In Roger van der Weyden's great *Last Judgment* at Beaune, the right hand of Christ that is raising up the Saved holds a flowering lily plant.
2. Pope-Hennessy in a letter in the Hyde Archives, December 9, 1963.

Provenance: First noticed by Marquand in the collection of Dr. Eduard Simon, Berlin, sold November, 1929; purchased from Paul Drey Galleries, New York, 1937.

Literature: Allan Marquand, *Luca della Robbia,* London, 1914, pp. 261-266, fig. 181; Wilhelm Bode, *Florentiner Bildhauer der Renaissance,* 3rd ed., Berlin, 1921, p. 159; M. J. Friedländer, E. F. Bange, and F. Schottmüller, *Die Sammlung Dr. E. Simon* (for Paul Cassirer and Hugo Helbring), Berlin, 1929, p. 88, pl. 34. (The preceding in English, *Catalog of the Collection of Dr. Eduard Simon,* same authors, dates and pages.); Royal Cortissoz, "Gems of the Renaissance in Sculptures Shown," The *Art Digest,* March 15, 1935, p. 12. (Illustrated as *Madonna with the Lilies.*); Alfred M. Frankfurter, *Exhibition of Sculptures of the Italian Renaissance,* A. S. Drey Galleries, New York, March 2-20, 1935, p. 10, no. 13, illustrated in frontispiece; *Pantheon,* XV, May 1935, p. 134, illustrated p. 180; William R. Valentiner, The Detroit Institute of Arts, *Catalogue of an Exhibition of Italian Gothic and Early Renaissance Sculpture,* Detroit, January 7 to February 20, 1938; George Henry McCall and William R. Valentiner, *Catalogue of European Paintings and Sculpture from 1300-1800,* "Masterpieces of Art Exhibition," New York World's Fair, 1939, p. 212, no. 426; "Art News Official Guide and Picture Book for the Masterpieces of Art Exhibition at the New York World's Fair," *Art News,* 1939, no. 19; S. Lane Faison, Jr., *Art Tours and Detours in New York State,* New York, 1964, p. 111, fig. 184.

Exhibitions: Kaiser-Friedrich Museums verein, Berlin, 1914; *Exhibition of Sculptures of the Italian Renaissance,* A. S. Drey Galleries, New York, March 2-20, 1935; *Exhibition of Italian Gothic and Early Renaissance Sculpture,* The Detroit Institute of Arts, January 7 to February 20, 1938; *Masterpieces of Art Exhibition,* New York World's Fair, 1939.

12. Andrea Mantegna ?

Italian, 1431-1506

Madonna and Child, c. 1464-70

Brush and ink heightened with white on brown paper, reworked with pencil.
29.2 x 19.7 cm. (11-1/2 x 7-3/4") 1971.73

This drawing was either derived directly from Mantegna by a contemporary follower or is by the master himself. The pose of the figures is exactly that of Mantegna's *Adoration of the Magi* (Uffizi, Florence), with the major changes occurring in the addition of a tree and the elimination of the grotto that surrounds the Madonna and Child in the Uffizi version. An unfinished early engraving also exists with the Madonna and Child, two of the kings, and the grotto, though the grotto is slightly changed from the Uffizi version. Executed by Mantegna's school, it may bear some relationship to the Hyde drawing.[1]

The draftsmanship and technique are characteristic of Mantegna's work. The use of toned paper with white highlights is an early example of what was to become standard practice in Venetian drawing at a later time. Characteristic of Mantegna's style is the handling of the drapery. Flat against the body, except where it breaks forward in folds, it is contrived to resemble one of the characteristics of the classical sculpture that Mantegna so avidly studied, to make prominent the shape of the human form.

1. An example of this engraving is in the Department of Prints and Drawings, Metropolitan Museum of Art, New York.

Provenance: Purchased from A. S. Drey Galleries, Munich, 1934.

13. Pellegrino di Mariano

Italian (Sienese), active 1449, d. 1492
(Formerly attributed to Giovanni di Paolo.)

Assumption of the Virgin Mary, c. 1475

Tempera and gold leaf on wooden panel. 27.3 x 19 cm. (10-3/4 x 7-1/2") 1971.19

The small scale of the *Assumption of the Virgin Mary* suggests that it once formed part of a larger, multi-panelled altarpiece dedicated to the Virgin Mary. Representations of the life of the Virgin were extremely popular and important subjects in Sienese art during the fifteenth century, for she was the divine patroness of the city much in the way that Athena was the patroness of Athens.

In Christian art the Assumption has special significance, since it ascribes to Mary a holiness almost equal to that of her son. She is thus revered because she was received into heaven immediately upon her death and was not required, like other mortals, to rest in her tomb until the Last Judgment. In Christian iconography the Assumption immediately precedes the Virgin's coronation as Queen of Heaven.

In this painting, even as she rises, two angels hold a crown suspended above her head. The musical angels are present as a sign of Mary's approaching royal role. They originate in the performing musicians that were the characteristic accouterment of the royal courts of Europe in the Middle Ages.

At the top of the painting, now cut off, an image of God the Father would most likely have appeared with his arms extended to receive Mary, as in Giovanni di Paolo's famous *Assumption* (Collegiata, Asciano).

The various instruments played by the angels have been identified by Albert G. Hess.[1] They are in ascending order: bottom tier left, cymbals—right, lute; second tier left, double shawm—right, double flute; third tier, a chorus of four angels sing; fourth tier left, a psaltry and drone fiddle—right, a half psaltry, and the instrument to the far right has been obscured by damage to the painting.

Although once identified with the work of Giovanni di Paolo,[2] Cesare Brandi more recently suggested it to be by Pellegrino di Mariano.[3] There are many aspects of the painting that would separate it from the style of Giovanni. The composition is too flat and too archaic to be his, and there is too great a stiffness and formality in the figures. By contrast, in Giovanni's *Assumption* at Asciano, Mary glances to her right while the angels move much more freely in space.

The condition of the painting is moderately good in spite of later paint which was applied in many passages.

1. Albert G. Hess, *Italian Renaissance Paintings with Musical Subjects,* New York, 1955, p. 6, pl. XCVI.
2. John Pope-Hennessy, *Giovanni di Paolo, 1403-1483,* New York, 1937, p. 174.
3. Cesare Brandi, *Giovanni di Paolo,* Firenze, 1947, p. 97.

Provenance: Paul Bottenweiser, Paris; August Berg Collection; purchased from Mortimer Brandt Galleries, 1950.

Literature: Pope-Hennessy, *op. cit.;* Brandi, *op. cit.;* Hess, *op. cit.;* S. Lane Faison, Jr., *Art Tours and Detours in New York State,* New York, 1964, p. 112, fig. 185.

14. After Desiderio da Settignano

Italian

The Christ Child, c. 1475

Wood, polychrome. 78.7 x 34.9 x 10.20 cm. (31 x 13-3/4 x 4") 1971.85

This is a copy in wood of the marble figure of the Christ Child that stands at the top of Desiderio da Settignano's *Tabernacle of the Sacrament* in the Church of San Lorenzo in Florence.[1] Desiderio's work was executed in 1471.

The infant Christ raises his right hand in benediction, while his left hand holds the crown of thorns and the nails that symbolize his Passion and Death.

Desiderio was one of the important sculptors in Florence in the Early Renaissance. He achieved a great reputation for his subtle renderings in marble of the features of women and children. This particular image of Christ, in which he appears both child-like and God-like, became quite popular and was copied many times. At Christmas time it is still displayed in the churches of Florence and Tuscany.

1. Research by Eleanor M. Hight.

15. Follower of Antonio Rossellino

Italian

Madonna and Child with Angels (The Barney Madonna),
late fifteenth or nineteenth century

Marble. 107.9 x 81.3 x 17.1 cm. (42-1/2 x 32 x 6-3/4″) 1971.100

In a subject common to Florentine fifteenth century art, the Christ Child is shown seated on the Madonna's lap, raising his hand in blessing. The Madonna is seated on a richly appointed throne and is accompanied by angels to indicate her role as the Queen of Heaven.

Although certified as authentic by W. R. Valentiner[1] and accepted with some hesitancy by Allan Marquand,[2] this sculpture has recently been described by John Pope-Hennessy[3] as a nineteenth century forgery. There is little question about this sculpture's association with Rossellino's style. The features of the face are similar to those of a portrait bust by Rossellino in the Staatliche Museum, Berlin-Dahlem. The composition paraphrases in reverse one of Rossellino's most famous relief sculptures of a Madonna and Child, the tondo from the tomb of the Cardinal of Portugal in S. Miniato, Florence. Pope-Hennessy sees the style as a blend of that of Rossellino's *Virgin and Child with Angels* (Kunsthistorisches Museum, Vienna), with that of one of Rossellino's followers known only as the Master of the Marble Madonnas.[4]

It is reasonable to conclude that the Hyde sculpture is not by Rossellino himself. Comparing the left hand of the Madonna in the Hyde work with the very similar right hand in the S. Miniato tondo, one finds in the authentic Rossellino a smoothness and continuity of form which is absent from the Hyde sculpture. From this comparison one can proceed to the more general observation that, whereas Rossellino's handling of marble produces a distinctive soft effect, the style of the Hyde work appears more hard-edged at a number of crucial points, including the face, hands, and feet of the Christ Child. Because of this decline of quality within what would be important passages, this relief would not even be accountable as the work of Rossellino's assistants.

John Pope-Hennessy sees as characteristic of nine-teenth century work, "the angels which overlap the moulding; the cherub head and the throne with a full putto on an arm." This may be true, but Pope-Hennessy seems to be in error when he relates the Hyde work to a terra cotta *Madonna and Child* (The Toledo Museum of Art), which he considers to be a forgery by the same hand, because the presence in both of a putto on the throne arm, and for the way the Christ Child appears peculiarly half-dressed in both works. The styles of the two works seem to be quite different, in spite of the similarity of motifs.

Another noted expert in Italian art, Creighton Gilbert, after carefully studying the Hyde sculpture in the original, expressed the verbal opinion that it was not a forgery at all, but rather the work of a somewhat later artist whose style was derived from Rossellino's.[5]

Pope-Hennessy presents convincing arguments that raise questions not only about the Hyde Rossellino, but also about numerous other sculptured reliefs attributed either to Antonio Rossellino or Desiderio da Settignano. Further investigation is necessary to determine whether or not the Hyde Rossellino must be included with this group. It seems not only superior to most forgeries, but also superior in general to most authentic fifteenth century Italian work. The problem of the attribution of the sculpture is further complicated by the fact that it is said to have been damaged by fire while in the Barney Collection and to have been subsequently repaired and cleaned of a film of carbon at French and Company, New York. The surface patina is certainly not correct, except in a few passages such as the little finger of the Madonna's left hand. It would appear that this piece had broken off before the fire, was stored where fire did not reach it, and then restored to the sculpture later. The Madonna's right thumb is lost. The forefinger of her left hand and part of the Christ Child's left foot have been replaced.

1. Letter from W. R. Valentiner, New York, February 1921.
2. Allan Marquand, "The Barney Madonna with Adoring Angels by Antonio Rossellino," *Art Studies,* II, 1924, p. 35.
3. John Pope-Hennessy, "Forging Italian Renaissance Sculpture," *Apollo,* CIX, April 1974, p. 252.
4. *Ibid.*
5. Letter from Creighton Gilbert, July 5, 1977.

Provenance: Charles T. Barney, New York; purchased from P. W. French and Company, Inc., 1923.

Literature: Marquand, *op. cit.;* Pope-Hennessy, *op. cit.*

16. Matteo di Giovanni di Bartolo

Italian (Sienese), 1435-1495

The Dance of Salome, c. 1480

Tempera and gold leaf on wooden panel. 27.3 x 37.4 cm. (10-3/4 x 14-3/8") 1971.28

The complete story of the feast of Herod and the dance of his daughter Salome appears both in the Gospels of Matthew (XIV, 3-12) and Mark (VI, 17-29). After John the Baptist stated that it was unlawful for Herod to have married Herodias, his brother Philip's wife, the angered Herod had John imprisoned. Herodias was particularly indignant and wanted John's death, but because of John's widespread reputation as a prophet, Herod hesitated to act. Then at a banquet celebrating Herod's birthday, his step-daughter Salome danced so well that Herod promised her anything within his power to grant. Influenced by her mother Herodias, Salome requested the head of John.

In the painting Salome dances while the executioner presents the head to Herod, thus the two key episodes of the story are combined for narrative clarity. Across the table from the executioner sits Herodias, while the remaining occupant is a serving man at the left who stands with his hand touching two ewers of wine.

The essential format of the subject was derived from Donatello's relief sculpture on the baptismal font in the Cathedral of Siena. Though the positions of Herod and Salome are reversed, there is the same theme of Salome dancing simultaneously with the presentation of the Baptist's head. The gesture of Herod is similar, the same table and lozenge-in-square floor pattern are present, and the same three arches are above and behind the foreground. In the Hyde painting, the background arches are represented as windows opening on to an architectural scene, whereas in Donatello's work, they open on to a room with figures.

The feast of Herod is often considered as a symbolic foreshadowing of the death of Christ, with Herod as a precursor to Pilate. In the Hyde painting this interpretation is implied by the reversal of the traditional arrangement of the subject, placing Herod in Pilate's usual position on the painting's left. The two ewers suggest the water with which Pilate washed his hands.

Matteo di Giovanni di Bartolo was in Siena not later than 1452. He had come from Borgo San Sepolchro, where he had collaborated with Piero della Francesca on Piero's altarpiece of the *Baptism of Christ,* executing the predella panels. While the central panel of the *Baptism* is in the National Gallery, London, the predella and wings remain in Borgo San Sepolchro. One predella panel illustrates the Feast of Herod, but with the arrangement as in Donatello's relief on the Siena font. Salome moves forward gravely, but does not dance. As in the Hyde work the space is divided into three sections by columns in the foreground plane, but these columns are rectangular, not circular in plan.

In the San Sepolchro predella, openings behind and above lead to a gallery with musicians. Such a gallery with musicians appears in Donatello's work, and is sufficiently common to the iconography of this subject to question the absence of the musicians in the Hyde version. It is as if the painting had not been completed, something implied also in the sketchy treatment of the forms.

When W. R. Valentiner certified the Hyde's *Dance of Salome,* he also certified a companion piece by Matteo di Giovanni showing St. Nicholas of Tolentino saving the miller's child from drowning. He further speculated that the two small paintings formed part of an altarpiece with the Madonna enthroned flanked by Sts. John the Baptist and Nicholas of Tolentino.[1]

For all its apparent sketchiness, the attribution of the painting to Matteo di Giovanni has not been questioned. In the picture are many characteristics of his style and composition, so it is certain that it at least comes from the artist's workshop. The loose treatment of the form, however, is not characteristic of this artist's highly finished style and suggests either that the painting is incomplete or that it has been crudely reworked by a later hand.

There is evidence that other scenes once flanked the *Dance of Salome.* Beyond an ornamental border on the right and left are the slight remains of further paintings. (See illustration.)

---

1. Letter from W. R. Valentiner, Detroit, August 10, 1943. Not listed in Fredericksen and Zeri (see below), the St. Nicholas panel seems to have disappeared.

Provenance: Purchased from Lilienfeld Galleries, New York, May 16, 1950.

Literature: Burton B. Fredericksen and Federico Zeri, *Census of Pre-Nineteenth Century Italian Paintings in North American Public Collections,* Cambridge, Mass., 1972, p. 139.

17. Andrea della Robbia

Italian (Florentine), 1435-1525

The Virgin Mary (Adoration), c. 1480

Glazed terra cotta. 80 x 32.3 cm. (31-1/2 x 12-3/4") 1971.98

Andrea della Robbia succeeded his uncle Luca as head of the famous Della Robbia workshop in the fifteenth century. Since few of the Della Robbia works have secure documents, there is always a problem of separating the work of Luca from that of Andrea. The Hyde *Adoration,* however, exhibits all the earmarks of Andrea della Robbia's style, and the excellent quality would make it one of the finest achievements by the master himself.

Much of Andrea's artistic fame rested with his portrayal of a youthful Virgin Mary, a subject he frequently repeated. In contrast, Luca's Madonnas are always both more mature and more full-cheeked, his facial types being derived in part from classical sources. A girlish Madonna was consistent with the Renaissance impulse to humanize the sacred personages of Christianity.

Unique among the Della Robbia Madonnas is the way this Mary almost rests back on her heels, causing the body to rise in an unusually graceful curve. Her body partly turns to a three-quarter position, adding complexity and tension to the motion. The drapery folds are arranged in perfect harmony with the pose, a refinement that is not encountered in examples executed by the Della Robbia workshop. The consummate grace of this work is reminiscent of the beautifully choreographed motion found in Botticelli's Madonna in the Uffizi *Annunciation* of 1489-90. Because of the general interest in a strong, graceful motion exhibited by Florentine artists of the period, this work seems to be appropriately placed in the 1480's, a time when Andrea would have been experimenting with a style more in accord with the latest artistic fashions.

This work is a fragment of what was once a larger composition. The Christ Child undoubtedly once lay on the ground to Mary's right. It is interesting to note here the observation of the scholar Wilhelm Bode, that Andrea della Robbia always placed the Christ Child to Mary's right, while Luca always placed him to Mary's left.[1] Characteristically the Madonna would have been set against a blue sky, which may have featured angels and a surrounding frame of leaves and fruit. This arrangement is apparent in a product of Andrea's workshop, the *Adoration* (Museo Nazionale, Florence). The Hyde *Adoration* is not a broken fragment, however, for Della Robbia reliefs were made in sections, and this work was fired as a single piece. The part including the Christ Child would have been fired with a section of the Madonna's robe behind him.

An *Adoration* from Andrea's workshop, described by Marquand as from the E. J. Berwind Collection, Newport, is the only other apparent example of a kneeling Madonna of the Della Robbias turning in a three-quarter position.[2] In this work the Christ Child is on a slightly forward plane and partly overlaps the Madonna's robe and knees. A curve of the Madonna's robe descends behind the child.

The condition of the Hyde relief is relatively good, however the glaze has been damaged in places and covered with patches of pale yellow paint. At one time it may have been covered entirely by this paint, or the paint may have been added by a clumsy restorer to conceal damage to the surface.

The pupils of the eyes are a solid dark blue, and the eyebrows were done with short strokes in a lighter blue. At the extreme left of the base, a small triangular piece of soft blue-green earth appears. The blue base is of wood and dates from the time the work was installed in the Hyde.

1. Wilhelm Bode, *Florentine Sculptors of the Renaissance,* London, 1908, p. 93.
2. Allan Marquand, *Della Robbias in America,* Princeton, 1912, p. 27, fig. 31.

Provenance: Purchased from Brummer Gallery, Inc., New York, January 6, 1936.

18. School of Hans Memling

Flemish, c. 1430-1494

Head of Christ, c. 1480

Oil on wooden panel. 14.75 x 11.6 cm. (5-13/16 x 4-9/16″) 1971.1

The portrait of Christ facing directly forward with outward staring eyes suggests, by implication, the theme of the enthroned Christ. Originating in Byzantine art, it persisted throughout the Middle Ages and Renaissance particularly in portrayals of the Last Judgment.[1]

The style of the *Head of Christ* is exceedingly close to that of Memling. It was common for Memling to present his more sacred figures in this fashion, staring straight ahead as do the images of Byzantine icons. It is quite possible that this head survives from a larger panel. In a recent cleaning a later gold halo was removed and the original blue background exposed.

The rendering, with its meager proportions and light modeling, demonstrates a still-persisting medieval embarrassment with the evident materialism of an over solid flesh. Yet the modeling that is present and the sharp descriptive details show that the artist had some ambitions to make his image true to reality.

The most recent observations about this painting convincingly relate it to a type of painting by Memling, *Christ Giving the Blessing,* of which two versions exist today (Norton Simon Museum, Pasadena; William A. Coolidge Collection, Topsfield, Massachusetts). Similarities among these works and the Hyde's *Head of Christ* "include the type and arrangement of hair and beard, suggestion of ears, gaze of eyes (and), drawing of lips . . ."[2]

The relation of the Hyde panel to Memling's style was first noted in 1942.[3] In 1964 it was attributed by Colin Eisler to Petrus Christus,[4] but the association with Memling or his school seems so apparent that it appears unlikely that it will be challenged.

1. Cf. the Tympanum at Vezelay Abbey, Roger van der Weyden's *Last Judgment* (Beaune), and Memling's own *Last Judgment,* Danzig.
2. Everson Museum of Art, *Medieval Art in Upstate New York,* Syracuse, 1974, pp. 73-74, no. 49, illustrated. Entry by Craig Harbison.
3. Letter from Ethelwyn Manning, Frick Art Reference Library, New York, September 1, 1942.
4. Colin Eisler, book review, *Art Bulletin,* XLVI, 1964, p. 104.

Literature: Eisler, *op. cit.;* Everson Museum, *op. cit.*

Exhibitions: *Medieval Art in Upstate New York,* Everson Museum of Art, Syracuse, 1974.

19. German or French

The Virgin Mary, c. 1485

Wood, polychrome. 76.2 x 54.6 x 28 cm. (30 x 21-1/2 x 11″) 1971.90

The placement of the head of this figure deep within the cowl that covers it and the angularity in the treatment of the drapery folds would place this sculpture within the last quarter of the fifteenth century. Although much of the naturalism of the Renaissance is present in the style, the many medieval artistic conventions identify this work as late Gothic.

A recent cleaning has revealed the original colors to be a soft blue in the Madonna's robe, a red in the undergarment, and a yellow green on the form on which she sits.

This devotional image presents many problems. The place of origin can only be generally designated North European since it has affinities with works of this period which were produced in Flanders, Burgundy, France, and Germany. Although a German source may be suggested by the angular drapery, the serene, idealized face is more common to French art.

One of the most intriguing aspects of this work is also one of the most puzzling. A figure seated in this fashion and holding a box has no iconographical precedent that can be identified. The box without a discernible lid is part of the single piece of wood from which the work is carved. It does not serve as a reliquary, but rather it must be read as an attribute or symbol.

It can tentatively be suggested that this subject is a symbolic pietà, with a small altar that may also be a sar-cophagus taking the place of the body of the dead Christ. The pietà with the dead Christ has always been considered a parallel to the theme of Mary holding the infant Jesus on her lap. A common subject of late Gothic art is that of Mary contemplating sadly the future death of her son. When the infant Jesus lies sleeping across her lap, it is a reference to the future when he will lie across his mother's lap in death. The tradition of rendering Christ's crib as an altar or as a sarcophagus decorated with an arcade originated in Carolingian times, appearing, for example, in ivory in the *Harrach Diptych* (Victoria and Albert Museum, London). It became common in Ottonian manuscript illuminations of the birth of Christ. Its persistence as a motif in German art further supports a German origin for this sculpture. In Germany also occurs the representation of the arcaded coffin in which the body of Christ was laid, as in Konrad von Soest's *Crucifixion with Scenes of the Passion and Ascension* in the church at Niederwildungen, Germany.

The pose of the seated Mary would instantly suggest a pietà, the head inclined, the hands held where they are commonly placed when she holds the body of Christ. Furthermore, rarely in Christian art are saints with attributes depicted in a seated pose, and even more rarely do their heads tip forward in this fashion. The pietà impression which the work produces is strong.

Provenance: Purchased from the Brummer Gallery, Inc., New York.

20. German

The Virgin Mary, c. 1500

Wood, polychrome. 63.5 x 18.4 x 16.5 cm. (25 x 7-1/4 x 6-1/2") 1971.86

What appears to be a figure of the Virgin Mary is portrayed as engaged in reading. Since the figure does not look outward, the statue was probably not intended to be an isolated cult image, but more likely it formed part of a large altarpiece. The subject of the Virgin with a book is common in fifteenth century Annunciation themes. If an Annunciation, in the original work the angel Gabriel would have been located somewhere to the figure's right, with Mary about to be interrupted in her reading. The colors of the costume, blue for the outer garment, red beneath, are those commonly associated with the person of Mary.

The calm isolation of the figure, the sense of mass in the form, and the harmonious drapery folds all suggest the influence of the Italian Renaissance. It is the facial type more than anything else that points to a German place of origin. Rounded, rather middle-class in appearance, the face lacks the characteristic idealizations of the French and Italian styles.

Literature: Everson Museum of Art, *Medieval Art in Upstate New York,* Syracuse, 1974, p. 56, no. 34, illustrated.

Exhibitions: Medieval Art in Upstate New York, Everson Museum of Art, Syracuse, 1974.

21. French ?

St. Peter Enthroned, c. 1475-1500

Oil on wooden panel. 31.1 x 21.6 cm. (12-1/4 x 8-1/2″) 1971.6

The subject matter of this painting is both unusual and puzzling. In Christian art St. Peter rarely appears enthroned. Usually it is the enthroned Virgin who represents the Church on earth. In the Hyde work it may be deduced that St. Peter has been substituted for Mary as the symbol of the Church. Four small sculptures representing the story of Adam and Eve adorn the pinnacles and arms of the throne. The subjects are: upper left, the creation of Adam; upper right, the creation of Eve; lower left, the temptation; and lower right, the expulsion from the Garden of Eden. Collectively they represent the realm of sin and death, the kingdom over which the Church presides. The temptation and expulsion from the Garden are themes customarily associated with the person of Mary who is the new Eve. (An Adam and Eve appear on Mary's throne in Jan van Eyck's *Madonna of Canon van der Paele,* Musées Communaux, Bruges.) The creatures at the base of the throne may be owls; they are not the characteristic lions of the throne of Solomon which often appear on Mary's throne. More likely they are references to sin, as were the owls in Bosch's paintings of the same period.

Peter holds his two attributes: his staff with a cross at the top and the pair of keys, one silver for the earth, one gold for heaven. The keys designate his role as the gatekeeper of heaven. He wears the three-tiered crown, the *triregnum,* and his royal robe, the *pallium.* Though difficult to decipher in the Hyde work, on the great clasp that holds the *pallium* would be represented the three rulers of heaven as they appeared in Christian iconography at the time: Christ, Mary, and John the Baptist (cf. Jan van Eyck's *Ghent Altarpiece,* St. Bavo, Ghent).

The surrounding architecture is itself a symbol of the Church. Behind Peter is the portal of a Gothic church, very similar to the double-doored portal in Roger van der Weyden's *Granada Altarpiece* with tympanum decorated with five narrow blind arches. On the *trumeau* of the portal directly above Peter's head, Mary appears wearing the crown as Queen of Heaven and carrying the Christ Child, the usual location of this image in the churches of Europe.

In the architrave are niches and pedestals for eight sculptures, but only three are filled. Of these, the broad handling makes it possible to recognize only the image of St. Andrew with his familiar attribute, the **X**-shaped cross.

The kneeling figure on the right of the painting appears to be tonsured and wears the robes of a monk. In his hands he holds his breviary. It seems most certain that he was the donor of the painting.

Behind the figure the world is represented by a conventional landscape in which a church tower appears that seems to reflect the architectural style of the Low Countries. (For example, the famous tower of Rhenen in Holland.) To add more confusion to the problems already raised, it may be noted that it is only in Dutch art of this period that this kind of broad brushwork appears, a distinguishing feature of the painting's style. Charles Sterling says the subject was common in the south of Europe and suggests possibly a Portuguese source.[1] This would seem, however, to be improbable on stylistic grounds. One could easily assume the painting to be German because of the strong, almost caricatured facial types. However, E. H. Havercamp-Begemann most recently reiterated what the majority of commentors on this work have felt—that it originated in Northern France.[2]

The coloration and the combination of architecture and figures resemble paintings by the French Master of St. Gilles. However, the broad brush work in many small passages of the Hyde work make the style unlike that of the Master of St. Gilles. The artists of Northern France invariably render every part of the painting with precision.

1. Letter from Charles Sterling, Dept. of Painting, Metropolitan Museum of Art, New York, October 4, 1943.
2. Letter from Havercamp-Begemann, Yale University, April 7, 1972.

Provenance: According to the catalogue of the Düsseldorf International Exhibit of 1904, the work originated in a Stein Collection, Cologne. In the Hugo Helbring sale catalogue, the Stein Collection is listed as in Worms. The Düsseldorf catalogue of 1904 shows that the painting was already in the Max von Heyl Collection, Darmstadt. The Helbring catalogue indicates that the maiden name of the wife of Max von Heyl was Stein. Thus it appears that it was her family who originally owned the work. The Helbring sale was in 1930; purchased prior to 1934.

Literature: *Düsseldorf International Kunsthistorische Ausstellung, Katalog,* Düsseldorf, 1904, no. 139, illustrated. Listed as "follower of Jan van Eyck"; Kaiser-Friedrich Museums verein, Berlin, *Katalog* (before 1930) under no. 552, *Death of the Virgin,* attributed to the Spanish master Bartolomé Bermejo; Hugo Helbring sale catalogue; *Sammlung von Antiquitäten . . . Gemälden alter und neuerer Meister . . .* from the collection of the late Max von Heyl and his wife Doris, Munich, 1930, p. 24, no. 155, pl. X; S. Lane Faison, Jr., *Art Tours and Detours in New York State,* New York, 1964, p. 112, fig. 187.

Exhibitions: International Kunsthistorische Ausstellung, Düsseldorf, 1904.

N principio creauit deus celum et terrã. Terra autem erat ina
nis τ vacua: τ tenebze erãt sup faciem abiffi: et spūs dñi ferebaf sup aĝs. Moyses diuinus pb a
latqz biftorie˚. q̃ troianu bellũ septingẽtis fere ãnis anteceffit edocet: quo de˚ machinatoz cõftitu:
torqz rex, cũ boc op˚ adoziretur: fecit pmũ oim celũ: et i fblime sufpẽdit: q̃ō eet sedes ipi˚ dei ozdtozis:
inde terrã fundauit: ac celo fbdidit. Tenebzas aũt cõftituit i terra. Nibil eñ ipfe ꝑtinet lumis:nifi accipiat
a celo. In q̃ pofuit lucẽ pennẽ: τ fuperos τ vitã ꝑpetuã. Et ꝗ̃ in terra tenebzas:τ inferos:τ morte. Moy:
fes vo cũ deu creaffe ꝗmemozat tres erroze Platonis.f. Ariftotilis τ epicuri elidit. Plato eñ ab eterno
veū ydeas ylen. Et in pncipio de yle mũdũ fuiffe factũ teftaf. ylen greci pmã materiã rex˚ nõ formatam ap:
pellãt. Qua vifibilia bec elemẽta formata funt.q̃ q̃dã ꝗeozdia ꝓueniut. Aũtqz ceteri de materia τ formā
aut ae atbomis factis fuiffe:de˚ tñ mũdũ fine placeri τ ꝑgata materia creauit: cũ prudẽtiffi˚ eet ad ex co
gitãdũ:τ ad facẽdũ folertiffi˚ antecqz ozdiref boc op˚ mũdi.qm̃ plen τ ꝗfummã boni fons i ipo erat:
vt ab eo bono tãq̃ riu˚ oztref. Angelos i pncipio oim creatura ꝑmozdiales feat. τ eo qõ ñ eꝫ:qz p eter
nitate foztꝫ eꝫ fortitudine ptãꝫ imefeꝫ: q̃ fue ac mõ caret:fic vita facturis. Quid ergo mirũ ñ facturus mũ
dũ:pus materiã de q̃ faceret ꝑpauit: ex eo qõ nõ erat. Q̃ō intellexerũt forte τ farracen̄ dicentes. Eductos
ãgelos a deo de tenebzis ad lucẽ:adipletoqz eterna leticia. In q̃bufdã tñ indolis diuie ftirpis nõ pmãfit.
Auctoꝛe bu˚ rei er bono ꝑ fe malũ effectũ greci diabolũ appellãt:nos crimi atoꝛẽ vocam˚. Terra erat ina
nis (vt trãftulit diu˚ Jˀiero. vł vt septingẽta) inuifibilꝫ τ icopofita: Quã ꝑ fu pbfidue abyffum vocat:quã
τ greca cbaos dicũt. Abyffum vocat terrã.i. materiã trino dimẽfu i altiffimas profunditates extenfam: de
boc etã Quid˚ meminit. Ante mare τ terras τ qõ tegit oĩa celũ. Uñ˚ erat toto nature vult˚ in orbe. Q̃ē
dixere cbaos rudis indigeftaqz moles. Nec ꝗqz nifi pödus inerꝫ: ꝗgeftaqz codẽ. Nõ bene iũctarũ difcoꝛ
dia femina rerũ. Nullus adbuc mũdo pbebat lumina titan. Et fpūs dñi:ꝑ qrganus diuine artis ferebaf fup
aquas:vt voluitas arcbitecti cũ cuncta ad faciendũ difponit. Cũ perfecta funt opa dei. Creatio rex fenario
numero explicatur. Cuius partes. vnũ:duo:tria funt. que in trigonũ furgãt. In primo creationẽ. In fe:
cundo τ tercio difpofitionẽ. In reliquis oznatum Moyfes per opera fex diez oftendit.

22. Michael Wolgemut, 1434-1519;

Wilhelm Pleydenwurff, d. 1494;
and, as author of the text, Dr. Hartmann Schedel, 1440-1514.
Anton Koberger, printer.

German

The Nuremberg Chronicle (Liber Chronicarium), 1493

Text: hand-illuminated initials and cast metal type;
illustrations: hand-colored woodcuts.
46.7 x 31.1 cm. (18-3/4 x 12-1/4") 1971.110

The *Nuremberg Chronicle* is an encyclopedia of world history and geography as it was understood at the threshold of the Renaissance. In a final colophon the author explains that the text "contains whatever deeds are worth noting from the beginning of the world down to the latest disasters of our own time." Interesting as a summation of medieval thought, the information is largely from legendary and sacred sources.

The designers of the *Chronicle,* primarily concerned with the visual appeal of the illustrations, scattered throughout the book six hundred and forty-five woodcut designs, many of which were printed more than once, for a total of 1,809 illustrations.

Two thousand copies of the *Chronicle* were printed, with editions in Latin and German. (The Hyde edition is in medieval Latin.)[1]

Erwin Panofsky and others have suggested that the German artist Albrecht Dürer, while he was an apprentice in Wolgemut's workshop for two years beginning in 1487, may have designed a few of the *Chronicle* illustrations.[2] Dürer's characteristic drawing style was undeveloped during that period, therefore identifying specific illustrations by his hand is highly conjectural.

The earliest publication to appear in bibliographical lists pertaining to American history is the *Nuremberg Chronicle* because of a reference on the back of folio CCXC. There is mention of a "New World" being discovered by a Martin Behaim of Nuremberg and a Jacobus Cam of Portugal. According to the *Chronicle,* during a voyage of discovery along the West coast of Africa, Cam and Behaim turned their ship directly west and found this "New World." While this would have been the voyage where Jacobus (Diogo) Cam discovered the Congo River, there is no evidence that Behaim was with Cam at the time, nor that the expedition ever turned west. It is generally believed that this passage was added by another hand. It was probably Behaim's presence in Nuremberg between 1490-93 that was responsible for the inclusion of this notation of discovery in the *Nuremberg Chronicle.* At the time he had been commissioned to make for the city what was to be the first terrestrial globe. It is almost exactly Behaim's map that appears in the *Chronicle,* folios XII and XIII, indicating his involvement in the project. Columbus had returned in March, 1493; the *Chronicle* was printed in July. Apparently this reference to a discovery of a New World was introduced into the *Nuremberg Chronicle* by Behaim as an attempt to steal Columbus' glory.

1. A Chicago lawyer, Walter W. Schmauch, has written the only English translation. Unpublished, it exists in the rare book room of the Free Library of Philadelphia.
2. Erwin Panofsky, *Albrecht Dürer,* Princeton, 1943, pp. 12-18.

Provenance: Earliest reference, December 1, 1931 in the Hyde Archives.

Literature: (the references are to other editions) Henry Harrisse, *Bibliothica Americana Vestustissima,* (books relating to America published between 1492-1551), New York, 1866, no. 13; Joseph Sabin, *Bibliotheca Americana,* New York, 1868-1936; Ludwig Friedrich Theodor Hain and Walter Arthur Copinger, *Repertorium Bibliographicum* (supplement), London, Sotharan, 1895-1902, no. 14508; Robert Proctor, *Index to the Early Printed Books in the British Museum,* London, 1898-1938, no. 2084; Campbell Dodgson, *Catalogue of Early German and Flemish Woodcuts in the British Museum,* London, 1903, I, p. 246-248; Alfred William Pollard, *Catalogue of Books Printed in the XVth Century Now in the British Museum,* London, 1908, II, no. 437; Wilhelm Ludwig Schreiber, *Handbuch der Holz- und Medallschnitte des XV Jahrbunderts,* Leipzig, 1926-27, no. 5203; Erwin Panofsky, *Albrecht Dürer,* Princeton, 1943, pp. 18-20; Ellen Shaffer, *The Nuremberg Chronicle,* Los Angeles, 1950; Walter W. Schmauch, unpublished translation, Rare Book Room, Free Library, Philadelphia.

23. Sandro Botticelli

Italian (Florentine), 1444-1510

Annunciation, c. 1492

Tempera on wooden panel. 17.8 x 26.85 cm. (7 x 10-9/16″) 1971.10

The small scale of this painting suggests that it may have once been part of the predella of an altarpiece. A number of similar small paintings of this sort by Botticelli exist. Of these, the most similar to the Hyde *Annunciation* is the *Annunciation* in the Lehman Collection (Metropolitan Museum of Art, New York).

The story of the Annunciation to Mary appears only in the Gospel of St. Luke. In Botticelli's presentation can be seen the angel Gabriel upon his arrival, with the angle of his descent still implied in his pose with draperies fluttering. Perhaps his greeting is implied: "Hail, thou art highly favored, the Lord is with thee: blessed art thou among women." (Luke, I, 28) Mary turns from her lectern with a receiving gesture, implying both her humility and her response to the angel: "Behold the handmaid of the Lord; be it unto me according to thy word." (Luke, I, 38) As in Botticelli's best works, the impression is one of highly controlled choreography, where the movements of the figures are as graceful as they are meaningful.

The subject of the Annunciation had come to be one of the most important in Christian art. It represented the point of Christ's Incarnation, where God became flesh, fulfilling the prophesy of Isaiah, VII, 14: "Behold a virgin shall conceive . . ." That the book read by the Virgin is a Bible open to Isaiah follows a description of the Annunciation in one of the most popular books of devotional writings in the late Middle Ages, the *Meditationes* by a Franciscan known as the Pseudo-Bonaventura. Before this, the book had been only a general reference to Mary's piety and to her wisdom. (The Byzantine Christian Church had equated Mary with the Greek goddess Athena.)

The architectural separation of Mary from the angel in the Hyde painting comes from a tradition in church decoration of placing the Angel of the Annunciation always on the left side of the chancel arch, and Mary across the nave on the right. In Gothic paintings the two figures were often portrayed in separate arched panels. The angel always appears on the church's and the painting's own right (the left side from the spectator's point of view), a traditional way in Christian iconography of indicating superiority in matters of divinity. However, by raising Mary on a slight podium, Botticelli subtly suggests her future role as Queen.

The architecture is formed of six groin-vaulted bays supported by three ranges of triple arches. The central range, an implied screen between Mary and the angel, cannot be seen because it is viewed head-on and is therefore concealed behind the central pier. A sequence of three arches was a stock symbol in the art of the time for the Holy Trinity. It appears here as a reminder of the theological point that the Incarnation of Christ was specifically brought about by the Trinity. The triple arch may also reflect a favorite way of referring to Mary as "Temple of the Trinity." That the purpose of the Incarnation was the redemption of man is revealed by the lilies which the angel carries. Principal flower of Paradise, the flower of Easter, and of funerals, the lily refers specifically to the Resurrection of Christ, and through Christ, of all proper Christians.

The walled garden that usually appears beyond the Annunciation in the art of the time had a double meaning. It is the closed garden of the Song of Solomon, a symbol of Mary's constant virginity (The Canticle of Canticles, IV, 12), but it is also a reference to the original sin, to the Garden of Eden, and to Mary's special role as the New Eve. Just as a woman once brought mankind down by tempting the First Man, so mankind is now to be redeemed by a woman. Often in Florentine art of the time, Adam and Eve actually appear in the background garden of the Annunciation scene, confirming this interpretation (cf. Fra Angelico's *Annunciation* of 1428, Diocesan Museum, Cortina).

The same strong architecture, painted a similar delicate gray-blue, appears in the Lehman Collection *Annunciation,* but in that rendering, the space is entirely closed, with only small arched windows at the back opening to a garden.

The painting appeared without any known provenance in The Hyde Collection in 1924, the year that it was published by Berenson in *Art in America.* Though damaged and somewhat reworked, it was subsequently accepted by Yashiro, Van Marle, Venturi, Gamba, Mesnil, Bettini, Salvini, Fredericksen, Zeri, and Lightbown. (See Literature below.) In 1959 the art conservator Morton Bradley removed the overpaint and restored the work to its present state, tattered but unquestionably authentic in all its parts.

Scholarly opinion has placed this painting at every stage of Botticelli's career: Gamba and Bettini, 1470; Yashiro, 1474; Berenson, 1480-81. Lightbown, however, after an exhaustive review of all of Botticelli's authentic work, has recently placed the work early in the 1490's, adjacent to the Lehman *Annunciation,* and closely related in style to it and to the tondo in the Ambrosiana, Milan.[1]

---

1. Ronald Lightbown, *Sandro Botticelli, Life and Work,* Berkeley and Los Angeles, 1978, II, p. 80, no. B70; I, pl. 40.

Provenance: Purchased 1924.

Literature: Bernard Berenson, "An Annunciation by Botticelli," *Art in America,* XII, June, 1924, pp. 180-189; Yukio Yashiro, *Sandro Botticelli and the Florentine Renaissance,* Boston and London, 1929, p. 56 and 239, no. 1474; Raimond van Marle, *The Development of the Italian Schools of Painting,* The Hague, 1931, XII, p. 150; Lionello Venturi, *Italian Paintings in America,* Milan and New York, 1933, II, pl. 244; Carlo Gamba, *Botticelli,* Milan, 1936, p. 113; Jacques Mesnil, *Botticelli,* Paris, 1938, p. 225, pl. LXVII; Sergio Bettini, *Botticelli,* Milan, 1942, p. 21; Roberto Salvini, *Tutta la Pittura del Botticelli,* Milan, 1958, I, pp. 41-2, tav. 31; S. Lane Faison, Jr., *Art Tours and Detours in New York State,* New York, 1964, p. 112, fig. 186; Burton B. Fredericksen and Federigo Zeri, *Census of Pre-Nineteenth Century Italian Paintings in North American Public Collections,* Cambridge, Mass., 1972, p. 34; Lightbown, *op. cit.*

24. School of Pietro Perugino ?

Italian

Madonna with Two Saints, c. 1493

Tempera on wooden panel. 78.1 x 60.3 cm. (30-3/4 x 23-3/4") 1971.32

The painting is nearly an exact replica, even to size, of Perugino's *Madonna and Child with Sts. Joseph and Catherine* (Louvre, Paris), with the exception that in the Hyde work, the St. Catherine has been transformed into a male figure and her palm branch has become a feather pen.

Recent investigation has indicated that: "The extensive overpaint in this panel makes any form of attribution meaningless. The condition of the original design below the broad reconstruction is considered poor. Numerous tests indicate this original surface to be greatly revised affecting content and style."[1] Thus, further discussion of this work must wait until it is possible to reveal what original paint remains.

1. Report from the Williamstown Regional Art Conservation Laboratory, Inc., 1978.

Provenance: Purchased from Jacob M. Heimann according to a letter of December 10, 1940. The letter states that Heimann "acquired this painting through an exchange with the Museum in Carpi, Italy. The Museum, however, purchased it from a noble family in Perugia."

25. Giacomo Cozzarelli ?

Italian

Madonna and Child, c. 1475-1500

Terra cotta. 55.9 x 48.2 cm. (22 x 19″) 1971.88

This is typical of a type of late fifteenth century Italian image of the Madonna and Child where the Christ Child stands on his mother's lap. The subject is unique in the way the Christ Child is positioned, turning away from his mother's embrace. There is a reference in this movement to the traditional Italo-Byzantine Madonna and Child type where the Child embraces his mother and presses his face against hers. This seems to be the position the Christ Child is turning from in the present work. It seems, too, that the Christ Child is about to assume another traditional pose, where he stands on his mother's lap and looks out and down, right hand raised in blessing. Thus the work represents Christ turning from one aspect of his nature to another: from his role as an utterly human child bound in affection to his mortal mother, to that of deliverer of divine grace to all mankind.

The attribution to the Sienese sculptor and architect Giacomo Cozzarelli must be considered, not so much a definite possibility, but rather as a starting point in determining the authorship of this terra cotta. Although Cozzarelli's name is inscribed on the frame, definite attribution is uncertain at the present. W. R. Valentiner saw the style as falling somewhere between that of Donatello and Luca della Robbia, and suggested the name of Michelozzo "where early works seem to go in style with these compositions."[1]

However, the strong turn in the body of the Christ Child indicates a later date. One is reminded of the pose of the Christ Child in Michelangelo's *Bruges Madonna* of 1503-04 (Church of Our Lady, Bruges).

1. Letter from W. R. Valentiner, Berlin, 1932.

26. Italian

Fountain, c. 1500 and late Roman ?

Marble. 220 x 101.6 x 40.6 cm. (86-5/8 x 40 x 16″) 1971.119

This characteristic wall fountain of the Italian Renaissance may once have been in the courtyard of an Italian palace, much as it is placed today in the courtyard of The Hyde Collection. Also it has been suggested that it may have served as a lavabo, the place where the priest washes his hands, in the sacristy of an Italian church. The marble is decorated in carved relief with grotesque heads, cupid heads, and leafy tendrils, all motifs common in Roman art. Charles Avery, Deputy Keeper of the Library of the Victoria and Albert Museum, London, was the first to note that the lower basin is in a different, earlier style. It is more roughly modeled than the work elsewhere on the fountain. The extensive use of incised lines and drill may suggest the possibility of late Roman work of the third or fourth century A.D.

In 1926, fourteen years after Hyde House was built, this fountain was placed against the east wall of the inner courtyard. The architects of the original house, Bigelow and Wadsworth of Boston (Henry Forbes Bigelow and Philip Wadsworth), directed the attention of the Hydes to the fountain in a letter from Henry Bigelow, February 16, 1926, in which it was referred to as the "Stanford White fountain." Bigelow mentioned a photograph of it installed in Stanford White's own home (St. James, Long Island ?), and stated that a similar fountain was in his Breese House on Long Island.

Provenance: Stanford White. Purchased 1926.

27. Anonymous, French

Triumph of Love, c. 1500

Tapestry, wool. 332 x 143.5 cm. (130-3/4 x 56-1/2″) 1971.116

This tapestry and a companion work in the Hyde, the *Triumph of Eternity* (see following entry), were originally the first and last in a series of six tapestries which depict a favorite medieval theme of human existence as six triumphs of fate over the individual. These triumphs were love, chastity, death, fame, time, and eternity. Of the series from which the Hyde has two fragments, two others, the *Triumph of Fame* and the *Triumph of Time,* survive in the Metropolitan Museum of Art, New York, but the *Triumph of Chastity* and the *Triumph of Death* have not been located.

The Hyde and the Metropolitan tapestries were originally from the collection of a Baron d'Ezpelata. The styles and techniques are exactly the same. It has been suggested that they were woven in France, probably in Touraine.[1]

Originally almost square in format, the left halves with the triumphal wagons are missing in both Hyde fragments. Their original appearance can be reconstructed because complete replicas of the Hyde/Metropolitan *Triumphs* and of the two missing tapestries survive in the Kunsthistorisches Museum, Vienna.[2] Originally on the left half of the *Triumph of Love* there would have appeared a four-wheeled wagon ridden by a blindfolded Cupid, seated on a canopied throne. In his left hand would have been a bow, in his right, arrows. The blindfolded Cupid represents mortal love, a love that is blind to love's true purpose, the love of God.

Beneath the wheels of the wagon would have been various mythological and Biblical personalities who had been conquered by love: Herodias, wife of King Herod; Solomon, Hercules, Paris, and Jason. Two richly dressed women representing voluptuousness and opulence would have turned the wheels of the wagon. In the surviv-

ing portion of the Hyde tapestry the lovers Pyramus and Thisbe are being trampled by the allegorical beings who draw the triumphal wagon. The procession is led by Venus who carries a harp, symbol of lust. The women with the tails of fish and the feet of birds are the sirens who tempted Ulysses with their songs. Behind them are two goats, also symbols of lust. The couple behind the goats are in a betrothal pose. Inscriptions identify them as *La Lubricité* and *Le Dépit,* lecherousness and spite. The man crosses the fingers of his left hand, possibly a reference to a common problem of the time, the seduction of young girls through false promises of marriage.

At the top of the tapestry was once a banner with four lines in French referring to the power of Cupid's bow.

This theme of human existence as six triumphs of fate is supposed to have been invented by the great fourteenth century Italian poet Petrarch in his famous series of six poems which he wrote over his lifetime and which were published together after his death as *The Triumphs.* However, it is likely that the theme may have had an even earlier source, possibly in a Gothic miracle play. Certainly Petrarch's descriptions of the triumphal processions are very different from what is depicted in the tapestries. Petrarch placed much greater emphasis on classical mythology. On the other hand, the tapestries appear to take their references from the popular allegory of late Gothic festival parades, in which people, dressed in costumes, would ride on wagons, to represent the various allegorical personalities. Thus, the triumphal chariot of the ancient Romans appears in the tapestries as a farm wagon, and apparently a common subject for these allegorical floats was that of the triumphs.

1. Joseph Breck, "The Tapestry Exhibition, Part II," *Bulletin of the Metropolitan Museum of Art,* New York, July 1928, XXIII, p. 184, no. 7.
2. *Art Treasures from the Vienna Collections,* loaned to the United States by the Austrian Government, 1949-50, p. 57.

Provenance: Said to be from the collection of the Baron d'Ezpelata, Chateau de Septmonts, Aisne, France; purchased from P. W. French and Company, Inc., New York, March 19, 1919.

28. Anonymous

French

Triumph of Eternity (Faith), c. 1500

Tapestry, wool. 315.8 x 215.2 cm. (125-1/2 x 85-3/4") 1971.115

(See preceding entry, the *Triumph of Love,* for a more complete discussion.)

The subject of this tapestry fragment portrays as much the idea of the triumph of the Roman Church, as it does of the triumph of eternity or of fate. As in the Hyde's *Triumph of Love* from the same series, there remains only the right half of this tapestry, but by referring to the replica in the Kunsthistorisches Museum, Vienna, one can see what the completed work was like. Symbols of the four Evangelists pull a triumphal chariot. Following ancient Christian tradition, the angel stands for Matthew, the winged lion for Mark, the winged ox for Luke, and the eagle for John. (Ezekial, I, 10, as presented to the prophet in a vision.) On the triumphal chariot, the wagon used when this theme was presented live in public festivals of the time, the Trinity once appeared in a burst of clouds and light, with God the Father at the top, the dove of the Holy Spirit directly beneath his beard, and Christ on the cross held by God's outstretched arms. Within the cloud enframement, a number of angels appear. Four Church Fathers, codifiers of Catholic theology, stand beside each of the wagon's four wheels. On the viewer's side of the wagon stand St. Ambrose at the front and St. Jerome at the rear. On the opposite side of the wagon stand St. Augustine at the front and St. Gregory at the rear. Beneath the four Evangelists and the wagon appear the principal triumphal figures discussed in the preceding entry, a traditional way of representing their defeat. Beneath the four Evangelists in the Hyde work can be recognized blindfolded Cupid, Atropos, the Fate who controlled death, and the magnificent winged woman who represents Fame. Behind them and beneath the wagon wheels, but no longer surviving in the Hyde example, were a woman dressed as a nun who represented Chastity, and a richly dressed Father Time. A young couple, not clearly identified, is beneath the rear wheels. They may stand for mortal love as opposed to spiritual love.

As indicated in the previous entry, the tapestry was woven in France, with its probable place of origin as the city of Touraine in the Loire Valley.

Provenance: See *Triumph of Love.*

29. French

Millefleurs (Love Garden), early sixteenth century

Tapestry, wool. 81.3 x 284.4 cm. (32 x 112") 1971.117

A garden was the usual setting for the love themes that were a popular subject of European tapestries of the fourteenth through the sixteenth centuries. The garden with erotic connotations originated in chivalric poetry, probably as a reference to the Garden of Eden, where love first occurred on earth. The animals that populate the garden in the Hyde tapestry, birds, dogs, and rabbits, were all associated with erotic love in the iconography of the period. Because of these references to love, garden subjects were the usual decoration for master bedrooms.

The style of the Hyde tapestry is here identified with the Loire ateliers, following the identification of a similar tapestry in the Williams College Museum of Art Collection.[1] However, the styles are not exactly the same, so the Hyde example is not a fragment of the tapestry at Williams.

It is a fragment nevertheless. When the Hyde tapestry was in the Henry C. Lawrence Collection, it was sixteen feet eleven inches long. Prior to acquisition, the length was reduced to nine feet four inches. One of the virtues of the millefleurs style was that the tapestry could be cut to fit the space required.

1. S. Lane Faison, Jr., *Williams College Museum of Art, Handbook of the Collection,* Williamstown, Mass., 1979, no. 20.

Provenance: Henry C. Lawrence Collection; purchased from P. W. French and Company, Inc., New York, April 26, 1921.

Literature: American Art Association, *Henry C. Lawrence Sale,* New York, 1921, no. 573, illustrated; Everson Museum of Art, *Medieval Art in Upstate New York,* Syracuse, 1974, p. 118, no. 83, illustrated. Entry by Priscilla Leggett.

Exhibitions: *Medieval Art in Upstate New York,* Everson Museum of Art, Syracuse, 1974.

30. Leonardo da Vinci

Italian, 1452-1519

Cartoon for the Mona Lisa, c. 1503

Silver point on grounded paper. Reworked in black chalk and graphite pencil.
62.2 x 50.8 cm. (24-1/2 x 20") 1971.71

Although almost all the visible work of the Hyde's *Mona Lisa* is by an inferior hand, evidence still points firmly in the direction of its being an original cartoon (a full-sized preparatory study) for Leonardo da Vinci's *Portrait of Mona Lisa* (Louvre, Paris).

The figures portrayed in both the drawing and the painting are exactly the same size,[1] though the drawing, which apparently has been cut down, is slightly smaller in overall dimension: 24-1/2 x 20 to 30-1/2 x 21".

When the *Mona Lisa Cartoon* was acquired by Mrs. Hyde from R. Langton Douglas in 1951, the small price suggests a recognition on the part of both that there were problems of authenticity. At the same time there was the compelling fact that the drawing had the same provenance as another portrait cartoon by Leonardo, the *Isabella d'Este,* in the Louvre. The Louvre cartoon is universally accepted as authentic. Both cartoons had been together in the collection of Giuseppe Vallardi, who stated that he purchased both from the Marquis Calderara-Pino.[2] The fact that both drawings are very close in size and are damaged around the edges in the same fashion from some early mounting, suggests they may have been bound together in the same album. Furthermore, since the two drawings made their first appearance in Milan (Calderara-Pino and Vallardi lived in Milan), the implication is that they had a Milanese history, possibly reaching back to Francesco Melzi, the original heir of Leonardo's drawings.

In 1860 Vallardi offered both drawings to the Louvre, but the museum accepted only the *Isabella d'Este,* probably because the Hyde cartoon had already sustained considerable damage and had been reworked by a later hand. Even more disturbing then, but today a most interesting aspect about the drawing, is that in many ways it was not like the famous portrait. Carlo Pedretti recently unearthed a reproduction of an early photograph of the Hyde drawing.[3] The subject in that reproduction has a rounder jaw, a broader nose, a lower dress, a graver expression, and eyes which look directly at the viewer. In short, there was a very different effect, even without considering the curious addition of the plant clumsily thrust into Mona Lisa's hands. The drawing in its present state confronts us with a final, crude reworking in which a desperate effort was made to bring its appearance into line with that of the painting in the Louvre.

That Pedretti's reproduced photograph and the Hyde drawing show the same work is certain, since both have the same divisions in the paper.[4] The Hyde drawing is formed of five separate sheets of woven paper, joined by a paste made of paper pulp. Because the drawing has not been mounted onto another sheet, the five parts are visible from the back. From the front the paper would have once appeared to be entirely smooth, having been covered with a ground to prepare it for silver point. However, after centuries of abrasion, the original divisions have worked their way to the surface.

Because the faces are not the same, Pedretti's old photograph taken before its last reworking proves certainly that the drawing is not a copy of the Louvre painting, as it first appeared to be. Had it been a copy, it still would have been executed in Leonardo's lifetime because silver point was universally abandoned as a medium by Italian artists early in the sixteenth century. If executed by Leonardo, the fact that the medium is silver point would place it quite early in the artist's career. It is Kenneth Clark's contention that Leonardo never did a silver point after the time of the *Last Supper,* which would have been in 1495 when he was working in Milan.[5] Silver point was Leonardo's favorite medium for portraits while in Milan, suggesting that at least the composition of the *Mona Lisa* might belong to an earlier date than the generally accepted 1503. Langton Douglas believes that Leonardo received the commission to paint Mona Lisa shortly after his arrival in Florence in 1500.[6]

Another vexing difference between the drawing and the painting is the plant alluded to earlier. It is doubtful that Leonardo did this himself, for there is not a drawing of a plant by Leonardo that does not have greater subtlety of form.

Pedretti sees the plant as a bay laurel, symbolizing the sitter's name or that of a possible patron, Lorenzo di Piero de'Medici.[7] However, the identifying shape of the bay leaf originally could not have been so clear because Vallardi, who owned the drawing before its disastrous final restoration, described the plant as a *canna,* a reed, with barely visible foliage. In addition, there is no known instance in Renaissance portraiture where the sitter's identifying emblem is so conspicuously held.

Possibly the meaning of this plant lies with the initial impression it would make on those familiar with Christian art. It resembles the palm branch that martyred Christian saints carried, usually over one shoulder, as in this drawing. However, the person portrayed here is not to be interpreted as a saint. The artist possibly used the old iconography to make a statement having mortuary connotations.[8] The palm branch, a reference to Eden and to the Tree of Life, represents the eternal life that is the martyr's reward, or the reward of any devout Christian. How this interpretation might apply in this instance is uncertain, though Langton Douglas notes that the Mona Lisa portrait was begun shortly after she had lost a child.[9]

A meticulous search for any sign of Leonardo's hand in the Hyde drawing as it appears at present is frustrated by the glossy graphite that veils every small passage. But at the point where the hair touches the right shoulder where it is crossed by the plant, delicate lines appear that have the characteristic warm tones of silver point. Vigorous, rhythmic, and curvilinear in impulse, these lines could qualify as an example of Leonardo's characteristic style. Elsewhere on the page a raking light reveals, here and there, the indentation of a line drawn in metal point. In these, possibly a ghost of Leonardo's hand vibrates almost imperceptibly behind the heavy-handed overlay.

One aspect of the visible draftsmanship that could or could not be attributable to Leonardo, is the large parallel shading strokes that appear in many passages. These descend from left to right in Leonardo's characteristic left-handed style. To Pedretti these lines were convincing. It must be noted here that these lines as they appear on the surface, even in the untouched areas to the right and left of the head, in actuality may not have been drawn at all. Instead they may be impressions of a coarsely-woven cloth.[10]

The problems pertaining to The Hyde Collection's *Mona Lisa Cartoon* may never be solved until technical developments make it possible to remove or get around the final reworking in some manner. Until that time, it cannot be studied apart from the early Pedretti photograph which exists only in a reproduced form. To study this would call for yet another reproduction, removing it even farther, in a platonic sense, from the reality that it represents.

At this writing, the painting in the Louvre itself requires cleaning and an in-depth technical study, but Carlo Pedretti's suggestion to do so has been rebuffed. Thus, one can only say that the final solution of the mysteries of the famous *Mona Lisa* must wait for another day.

1. Carlo Pedretti, *Leonardo da Vinci: Studies for the "Mona Lisa Cartoon" with Drawings after Leonardo from the Elmer Belt Library of Vinciana,* Los Angeles, 1973, p. 21.
2. Giuseppe Vallardi, *Disegni di Leonardo da Vinci,* Milan, 1855, pp. 65-66. Cited in Pedretti (see note 1, above).
3. Pedretti, *op. cit.,* p. 21, fig. 7. Carlo Pedretti discovered the photograph reproduced in *Illustrazione Italiana,* Milan, September 3, 1911, pp. 238-239, in an article written by an unnamed author. The photograph came from a Milanese antique dealer, Carlo Clerici, who had received it from Vallardi's son. Pedretti dates the photograph around 1889. In the article the drawing is described as already reworked even at the time of the photograph.
4. *Ibid.,* fig. 7.
5. Kenneth Clark, *The Drawings of Leonardo da Vinci in the Collection of Her Majesty the Queen at Windsor Castle,* 2nd ed., revised with the assistance of Carlo Pedretti, London, 1968, p. XXVI.
6. R. Langton Douglas, *Leonardo da Vinci,* Chicago, 1944, p. 29.
7. Pedretti, *op. cit.,* p. 38.
8. Leo Steinberg, "Leonardo's *Last Supper*," *Art Quarterly,* XXXVI, Winter, 1973, p. 297 ff., has convincingly demonstrated Leonardo's interest in iconographical matters.
9. Langton Douglas, *op. cit.,* p. 29. First mentioned by E. Muntz, the death was to have occurred in 1499.
10. An observation made by Marilyn Widener, paper conservator, 1973.

Provenance: The Hyde drawing has a firm provenance extending back to the eighteenth century in Milan, to the Marchese Calderara-Pino, from whom Giuseppe Vallardi tells us he purchased the *Mona Lisa* and *Isabella d'Este* cartoons. (Vallardi, *Disegni,* . . . see Literature.) Vallardi's collector's mark appears in the drawing's lower right. The Vallardi Collection was sold at Paris in December, 1860, but Pedretti says the Hyde drawing did not leave Italy until 1893. It must have been at this time that it was acquired by Baron J. Vitta and brought to Paris. That Langton Douglas purchased the drawing from Baron Vitta is implied in his own book on Leonardo. There (Plate XLIX) in 1944, he has the drawing as in the Vitta Collection where in fact he must have owned it by 1939, since he is recorded as the lender of the drawing to the Leonardo exhibit held in Milan that year; purchased from Langton Douglas, 1939.

Literature: Giuseppe Vallardi, *op. cit.;* Charles Blanc, *Gazette des Beaux Arts,* IX, 1861, p. 72; Eugène Muntz, *Leonardo da Vinci, L'Artiste, le Penseur, le Savant,* Paris, 1899, p. 511 (in the revised English edition, II, p. 246); Charles Ravaisson-Mollien, *Bulletin de la Societé Nationale des Antiquaires de France,* 1909, pp. 275-276; Charles Ravaisson-Mollien, "Le Carton de la Joconde et la Collection Vallardi," *Bulletin des Musées de France,* 1909, p. 37; Salomon Reinach, "La Tristesse de Mona Lisa," *Bulletin des Musées de France,* 1909, p. 18; *Illustrazione Italiana,* Milan, September 3, 1911, p. 239, illustrated; Salomon Reinach, *Revue Archeologique,* XXII, 1913, p. 410; Seymour de Ricci, *Gil Blas,* January 1, 1914; Giovanni Poggi, *Leonardo da Vinci, La Vita di Giorgio Vasari Nuovamente Commentata e Illustrata,* etc., Florence, 1919; R. Schneider, *Études Italiennes,* Paris, 1923, p. 207; Heinrich Bodmer, *Disegni di Leonardo,* Florence, 1939, p. 17, pl. 23; *Mostra di Leonardo da Vinci Catalogo,* Milan, 1939, p. 160; Stefano Bottari, *Leonardo,* Bergamo, 1942, p. 36, pl. 122; R. Langton Douglas, *Leonardo,* Chicago, 1944, p. 29, pp. 39-40, pl. XLIX; Odoardo H. Giglioli, *Leonardo,* Florence, 1944, p. 79; Los Angeles County Museum, *Leonardo da Vinci Loan Exhibition,* 1949, pp. 115-116, no. 92; Musée de Louvre, *Homage à Leonard de Vinci,* Paris, 1952, p. 26; Giorgio Castelfranco, *Leonardo Saggi e Ricerche,* Rome, 1954, p. 468, note 61; Carlo Pedretti, *L'Arte,* LVIII, 1959, pp. 159, 186, note 1; Barbara Bacall, *A Catalogue of the Drawings of Leonardo da Vinci and His School in the United States,* unpublished M.A. thesis, University of California, Los Angeles, 1968, no. 9; Pedretti, *op. cit.,* pp. 17-22; catalogue pp. 34-39, figs. 7 and 8; *Gazette des Beaux Arts,* Paris, LXXXIII, January, 1974, p. 23, fig. 20; Denys Sutton, "Robert Langton Douglas, Part IV," *Apollo,* CX, July, 1979, p. 18, fig. 42.

Exhibitions: *Mostra di Leonardo da Vinci.* Palazzo dell'Arte, Milan, May-October, 1939. *Leonardo da Vinci Loan Exhibition.* Los Angeles County Museum of Art, Los Angeles, June 3-July 17, 1949. *The Genius of Leonardo.* Virginia Museum of Fine Arts, Richmond, November 30, 1951-January 6, 1952. Fogg Art Museum, Cambridge, Mass. n.d. Elmer Belt Library, University of California at Los Angeles, April, 1973.

31. Raphael Sanzio

Italian, 1483-1520

Portrait of a Young Man, c. 1511

Oil on canvas. 42.5 x 32.9 cm. (16-3/4 x 12-15/16") 1971.36

Approximately twenty portraits survive by Raphael's hand. These may be divided into two categories, the first of which includes the formal portraits representing important persons. These are larger in scale, and include both of the subject's hands. Often one of the hands is shown holding a piece of paper or a significant attribute. The most famous of these attributes in a Raphael portrait is the magnifying glass in the hand of *Pope Leo X* (Uffizi, Florence).

There is a lesser group of smaller, more informal and more personal portraits in which hands do not appear. The earliest of these is the *Portrait of a Man* (Galeria Borghese, Rome), dated 1503-04. The latest, tentatively accepted by Dussler and possibly of the engraver Marcantonio Raimondi[1] (Compte L'Estang de Parade, Aix-en-Provence), seems quite similar in concept to the Hyde work.

Of similar size and format is Raphael's famous self-portrait (Uffizi, Florence), but this has been so extensively reworked by later hands that its authenticity must remain in doubt.

Because of a similarity in cap, in hair, and in facial type, the Hyde portrait has been associated with Raphael's *Portrait of Angelo Doni* (Pitti Palace, Florence).[2] This association probably accounts for Dussler's dating the Hyde painting at the end of Raphael's Florentine period. While Fischel would date it at the same time or "at the very beginning of the Roman period," he placed it in his catalogue with paintings he believed were done by Raphael around 1511.[3] If by Raphael, this painting would have been executed no earlier than 1511. By this time his work in fresco had affected a greater breadth, simplicity, and effect of the third dimension in his style. The face in the Hyde portrait is different from that of Angelo Doni for these very factors. A simplification, deepening, and strengthening of the form in the rendering of the eyes is particularly apparent. It is also to be noted that in all of Raphael's male portraits before his Roman period, a landscape appears behind the figures, while after his arrival in Rome, the background is more often a neutral field. However, that field has the substance of a wall as is indicated by the shadow cast against it, both in the Hyde portrait and in the *Portrait of Castiglione* (Louvre, Paris). In more than half of Raphael's portraits, male figures are shown turning to the right while their eyes glance to the left. Furthermore, this is the position in which Raphael portrayed himself in his two self-portraits, the drawing as a boy (Ashmolean Museum, Oxford), and in the group of figures on the right in the *School of Athens* in the Stanza della Segnatura (Vatican, Rome). To the list of portraits posed in this way may be added the *Angelo Doni* and the so-called *Portrait of Marc-*

antonio Raimondi discussed above, where the presentation is comparable though reversed. Similar poses occur in his female portraits as well, to the point where one may consider such a pose as a stock convention of the artist. Its origin lies in Leonardo da Vinci's *Mona Lisa,* where there is the same turn to the right and glance to the left.

Such a pose has subtle and telling connotations, particularly in the Hyde portrait. Calm, but slightly tense, the expression gives a vivid impression of a mind engaged in thought. The clarity of the forms and the sober black and gray hues act in accord with this expression of calm reason. Glancing to the side, the portrayed image is psychologically disconnected from the spectator and the external world. The thinker is appropriately isolated in a higher realm of thought; and yet, in a way utterly appropriate to the Renaissance concept of man in his relationship to the world, the sitter seems to be partly drawn by some distraction to his right. A link to the world is thus established. Subtly the artist places his sitter at a point midway between the spiritual and the physical, the spiritual being largely an intellectual matter.

While the authenticity of this painting was accepted without reservation by Oskar Fischel[4] and with some reservations by Dussler,[5] who was not able to inspect the original, it has been questioned informally by others; significantly by Sidney Freedberg. Freedberg suggested the possible authorship of Raphael's close imitator Ridolfo Ghirlandaio.[6]

In a laboratory analysis of this painting, still unfinished at the time of this writing, X-rays have revealed a curiously crude preliminary painting beneath the finished work. It is as if Raphael himself had extensively reworked a portrait painted by an assistant. Though this is not offered as an explanation, the style of the visible painting is certainly close to Raphael's. As one moves across a face painted by Raphael, certain peculiarities of treatment become evident. The closest comparison would be with the *Portrait of a Cardinal* (Prado, Madrid), where there are so many similarities that it could be the same face if the chin of the Hyde portrait subject were somewhat longer and the nose less broad. The telling similarities lie in the sequence of light and shade around the eyes, the painting of the lines around the left eye, and in the folds of flesh framing the mouth. A greater simplicity and breadth would be due to the more informal purpose of the Hyde work. Quite comparable, too, is the rendering of the face of Agostino Beazzano in Raphael's double-portrait (Doria Gallery, Rome). Dussler and Fischel both date the *Portrait of a Cardinal* around 1511, the same date that is herein assigned to the Hyde portrait. The double portrait is dated 1516. Unfortunately, one of the most characteristic aspects of Raphael's style in the Hyde portrait, the rendering of the hair in the artist's characteristic warm, brown, translucent, curvilinear manner, appears to be later work, possibly done with an intent to mislead. While serious questions must be raised at this point as to the painting's authenticity, its acceptance by such experts as Fischel, and the distinctly Raphaelesque manner of the style, require that the matter remain open until pigment analysis is available.

The condition of the painting is good. Although it was retouched in small spots over the entire surface, the general impression remains unaffected. Recent laboratory study suggests that the painting, now on canvas, was possibly transferred from a panel.

1. Luitpold Dussler, *Raphael: A Critical Catalogue of His Pictures, Wall Paintings, and Tapestries,* London and New York, 1971, p. 33, pl. 81.
2. *Ibid.,* pp. 17-18.
3. Oskar Fischel, *Raphael* (English translation of the 1948 ed.), London, 1964, I, p. 362.
4. *Ibid.*
5. Dussler, *op. cit.,* p. 17, pl. 22.
6. Sidney Freedberg in a conversation with former curator of The Hyde Collection, Joseph Dodge.

Provenance: W. C. Whitney (Probably William Collins Whitney, Secretary of the Navy under President Cleveland.); purchased from Agnew and Sons, London, Ltd., 1938.

Literature: *Arundel Club Portfolio,* 1904, pl. 1; Fischel, *op. cit.;* Dussler, *op. cit.;* Burton B. Fredericksen and Federico Zeri, *Census of Pre-Nineteenth Century Italian Paintings in North American Public Collections,* Cambridge, Mass., 1972, p. 172; Wilhelm Kelber, *Raphael von Urbino, Leben und Werk,* Stuttgart, 1979, pp. 139, 431, no. 61, illustrated p. 119.

32. Flemish

Antwerp Mannerist School

Adoration of the Kings, c. 1520

Oil on wooden panel. 62.6 x 52.2 cm. (24-5/8 x 20-9/16″) 1971.2

The Adoration of the Kings became one of the most popular subjects in the art of Northern Europe in the late Middle Ages, possibly because relics of the three Magi were housed in Cologne Cathedral, a famous pilgrimage shrine, and also because the pageantry of the theme resembled so much the pageants that were performed on important public occasions in the cities of Europe at the time. Earlier the story of the three kings had become a favorite one for religious plays because of the many allegorical connotations that had accrued to the subject over the centuries of Christian art.

In Byzantine times the theme of the Magi bearing gifts to the infant Christ acquired its epiphany significance, the three magicians became the three kings, and this subject came to represent the point when the true religion transcended its narrow Jewish origins and was established among the Gentiles. The classical architecture enframing the scene, which became very ornate in the paintings of the Antwerp Mannerists, represents the new church that is coming into being, while the ruined architecture in the background represents the decaying synagogue. The ox usually symbolizes those who have accepted Christ while the ass symbolizes the Jews who rejected him.

When the Magi became kings, this was to demonstrate how the nations of the earth submit themselves to the authority of Christ, the universal King. In a later evolution of the subject in the Middle Ages, the three kings came to represent the three known continents of the earth. A Negro came to stand for Africa, probably due to the existence of the ancient Christian Church in Ethiopia. Somewhere in the evolution of this subject, the kings had acquired their names, Melchior, Caspar, and Balthasar. Thus in its final form, the Adoration of the Magi came to be far removed from the Biblical description of the visit of the Magi, which occurs only in the Gospel of Matthew (II: 1-12).

The Adoration of the Kings came also to stand for the Nativity of Christ, replacing in the early fifteenth century earlier representations which depicted Mary lying down, while in the foreground the newborn Child is being washed. In the Hyde work Christ's birth is referred to by what came to be a popular symbol in this subject, the arched opening in the immediate foreground. Usually portrayed with a grillwork of iron bars, it imitates descriptions brought back by pilgrims of the grotto of the Nativity, the shrine in the Church of the Nativity in Bethlehem that supposedly is the cave or cellar in which Christ was born. An earlier interpretation of the grotto referred to it as the burial cave where the dead await the salvation that Christ was sent to deliver to mankind.

In the central background the procession of the kings approaches from Jerusalem, where Herod has just been questioned by the Magi. Jerusalem can always be recognized in Christian art by the presence of a two-tiered circular building, a rough approximation of the appearance of the shrine of the Holy Sepulchre. This building still marks the site of the cave in which it is believed Christ had once been buried.

So many similar paintings or exact replicas of the Hyde work exist that Max J. Friedlaender organized them all into groups and categories.[1] The Hyde Collection painting, though not discussed by Friedlaender, belongs with his group "C" which revolves around a close replica in the John G. Johnson Collection (Philadelphia Museum of Art). Philadelphia attributes this painting to the "Master of the Groote Adoration." The Hyde painting, similar in composition, is not similar in style. It is closer to, though finer than, a version in the Metropolitan Museum of Art, New York.

The variations on this format are often in triptych form. This may have originally been the case with the Hyde work. In a Jan de Beer version (Brera Gallery, Milan), the left wing depicts a Madonna and angels adoring the Christ Child, while on the right appears a scene representing the Rest on the Flight into Egypt. In a still closer variation on the Hyde work attributed to the Master of the Groote Adoration, and sold on May 16, 1980 by Galerie Koller, Zürich, Mary adores the Child alone in the left wing, while on the right is depicted the Flight into Egypt.

While in generally good condition, several passages of the Hyde painting have been reworked. The red cloak of Joseph has been largely repainted. Perhaps this was done by the art restorer to whom the painting was sent in 1939 when a crack down the center was to be repaired. From an earlier photograph it is known that this restorer repainted the Madonna's face in an unfortunate manner, destroying its attractiveness.

---

1. Max J. Friedlaender, *Jahrbuch der Königlich Preuszischen Kunstsammlungen,* Berlin, 1915, XXXVI, p. 78.

Provenance: Purchased from E. and A. Milch, Inc., New York, 1929.

33. Bartel Beham

German, 1502-1540

Portrait of Philipp von der Pfalz, Bishop of Freising, c. 1528

Oil on wooden panel. 43.1 x 35.5 cm. (17 x 14") 1971.7
Inscribed at top: "PHILLIPPVS COM PALAT DVX BAV EP FRISINGENSIS."

The inscription at the top of this painting identifies the sitter and may be translated as "Philipp, Count Palatine, Bavarian Prince, Bishop of Freising." Philipp von der Pfalz was born in 1480 and died in 1541. Pfalz is the German designation of the Palatine, the Western German state under the control of the Duke of Bavaria.

A replica of the Hyde painting, but with a landscape background, appeared in 1912 in the Friedrich Lippman sale in Berlin. There the portrait was identified as "Philipp von der Pfalz, Bavarian prince and archbishop of Freising."[1] The town of Freising, with its great early cathedral, is in Bavaria, a short distance north of Munich.

It was in 1527 that Beham became the official painter to Duke Wilhelm IV in Munich. While in this post he painted many portraits of the ducal court. By this time he had already distinguished himself as an engraver, a close follower of Albrecht Dürer, as was his more famous elder brother, Hans Sebald Beham.

The Hyde portrait reflects the difficulty German painters experienced in transcending the limitations of an earlier painting style derived from Flanders. A general lack of spacial effects and an emphasis on line over mass are elements in this portrait that give it an archaic appearance quite different from Dürer's own richly modeled forms.

In the face itself one sees the direct, unflattering realism characteristic of the German style. Also characteristically German is the curious intensity of the expression. In the eyes there is a fixed stare that suggests a kind of nervous spirituality quite unlike the calm intellectuality that pervades Italian High Renaissance portraits.

Placing figures against a blue green background is a typical portrait convention in North European art of the time. One sees it in the Bartel Bruyn and Corneille de Lyon portraits in The Hyde Collection (numbers 34 and 35 in the catalogue).

1. Sammlung Friedrich Lippman, *Versteigerung,* November 26, and 27, 1912, Rudolph Lepke's Kunstauctions-haus, Berlin, no. 23.

Provenance: Madame Costanzo, Paris; Duc d'Aumale; Lawrie and Company, London; Dowdeswell and Dowdeswell, London; Joseph and Kate Davis Pulitzer; purchased from E. and A. Milch, Inc., New York, 1932.

Literature: American Art Galleries, *The Dowdeswell and Dowdeswell and Blakeslee Collections,* New York, April 7 and 8, 1904, no. 7; American Art Association, *Oil Painting by XVII and XVIII Century Masters, Collection of the Late Joseph and Kate Davis Pulitzer . . . ,* New York, 1929, no. 26; Charles C. Kuhn, *A Catalogue of German Paintings of the Middle Ages and Renaissance in American Collections,* Cambridge, Mass., 1936, p. 57, no. 217; S. Lane Faison, Jr., *Art Tours and Detours in New York State,* New York, 1964, p. 113, fig. 188.

34. Bartel Bruyn

German, 1493-1555

Portrait of a Young Woman, c. 1535

Oil on wooden panel. 30 x 22.9 cm. (12-5/8 x 9-3/32″) 1971.11

The pose of the woman in the Hyde portrait, almost frontal, with a flower in her right hand and with the fingers of the left neatly together, was common in Bruyn's style to the point of being an artistic convention. It was a more general convention of the time that the women in portraits invariably turn to their right, suggesting the position of the figure of Eve to the left of the Tree of Knowledge in the traditional arrangements of the subject of the Temptation in the Garden of Eden.

In Bruyn's double portraits of husband and wife, the husband is always to the viewer's left, and turning to his own left, the traditional position of Adam. That this was not such a double portrait, with its male half missing, is indicated by the fact that the young girl appears to be unmarried; she does not wear a wedding ring on the third finger of her left hand. Bruyn's other portraits of married women indicate that this was as much a custom in sixteenth century Germany as it is today. Nor is the girl in the Hyde portrait coiffed in the white linen of a wife. She wears instead the ornamental headdress of an unmarried woman.

The flower offered is reminiscent of the flower offered by the allegorical figure in Raphael's *The Knight's Dream* (National Gallery, London), where the female figure represents the pleasures of life. Erwin Panofsky interprets the flower symbol in a similar portrait of a young girl by Albrecht Dürer, *Katharina Fürlegerin* (Staedelsches Kunstinstitut, Frankfort), as symbolizing *Voluptas* (sexual pleasure) and explains it as a way of making a statement about the young lady's desirability in marriage.[1] At the same time the slightly downcast eyes in the Hyde portrait suggest *Castitas* (chastity) or modesty, a second desirable quality in a young girl, for all the reverse implications of the flower. It may then be that the function of this portrait was to serve as a means of introducing the young lady to a potential suitor.

The artist, Bartel Bruyn, was mentioned as early as 1519 as one of the most important members of the painters guild in Cologne. In 1550-53 he was an elected member of the city council, another indication of his prominence.

Bruyn's religious subjects show the influence of the Flemish painter Joos van Cleve. More generally, the influence of Flemish art was great in Germany at the time. While Bruyn's work has often been mistaken for that of the great German portraitist Hans Holbein, Bruyn's style, less spacial in every respect and less psychological, has far less of the Renaissance in it.

Max Friedlaender certified the authenticity of the painting in 1925 and 1926.[2]

1. Erwin Panofsky, *Albrecht Dürer,* Princeton, 1945, p. 41.
2. Max Friedlaender, the Hyde Archives.

Provenance: Purchased from E. and A. Milch, Inc., New York, 1929.

Literature: Alfred M. Frankfurter, "Bartel Bruyn in American Collections," *The Antiquarian,* XIV, March, 1930, pp. 61 and 86, illustrated, p. 58; Charles Kuhn, *A Catalogue of German Paintings of the Middle Ages and Renaissance in American Collections,* Cambridge, Mass., 1936, p. 27, no. 24.

35. Corneille de Lyon ?

French, of Dutch descent, active 1533-74

Portrait of the Count d'Angoulême, c. 1560

Oil on wooden panel. 21 x 15.8 cm. (8-1/4 x 6-1/4") 1971.14

This portrait of a French aristocrat is identified as the Count d'Angoulême by an old label on the back of the frame. With no evidence to the contrary, there is reason to retain this identification.

The costume and closely cut hair place the painting in the middle of the sixteenth century; the style and format relate it to a number of portraits of the French nobility attributed to the painter Corneille de Lyon. The only documented work by Corneille is of a Pierre Aymeric, dated 1533 (private collection, Paris).[1]

The artist was born in The Hague, Holland, the date unknown. He appears in documents in 1540 as painter to Henry, the *dauphin* of France, who later became King Henry II. In 1547 Corneille became a French citizen. The artist continues to appear as a portraitist for the French Court through the reigns of Henry II (1547-1559), Francis II (1559-60), and Charles IX (1560-74). With the termination of the reign of Charles IX in 1574, Corneille de Lyon vanished from the scene of history.

One of the few contemporary documents that refers to Corneille was a notation by the Venetian ambassador to France, Giovanni Capelli, who visited the artist's studio in 1551. He refers to seeing here "little portraits" of all the members of the French Court.[2] Based upon this observation, a body of small portraits of the French aristocracy, which seems to show more of a Dutch than French style, has been attributed to Corneille de Lyon. In these portraits the backgrounds are usually green in the Dutch manner. The paintings are framed in many instances, as is the Hyde portrait with little columns of marble flanking the panel, with an entablature across the top.

The Venetian ambassador's comment suggests that Corneille must have accumulated a collection of master images for his studio from which he could, when required, make replicas. The presence of masters and replicas among Corneille's oeuvre may account for the fact that among the attributed works two styles can be distinguished. In the category that includes the Hyde portrait, the handling of paint is somewhat broader and more rapid. Certain indications of clumsiness appear, such as in the rendering of the ear. The same style appears, for example, in the portraits attributed to Corneille of *Moretto da Brescia* (Walter Gay Collection, Paris); of *Mareschal Bonnivet* (The Toledo Museum of Art); of *Monsieur de la Nève* (Metropolitan Museum of Art, New York); and in the *Portrait of a Prelate* (National Gallery of Art, Washington, D.C.). To the second stylistic category belongs the beautiful portrait of the *Countess of Longwy* (Museum of Fine Arts, Boston). Here the style is smooth and clear, without breadth or clumsiness. Perhaps the more time-consuming and finished style represents the replica, while the broader style may be that of the studio master copy, taken rapidly and directly from life. It may be argued, however, that the reverse is true, that replicas are generally less finished than are originals.

A curiosity of these paintings is the frequency with which the same male facial type appears. The Hyde portrait shows great similarities to the *Moretta da Brescia,* the *Marechel Bonnivet,* or the *M. de la Nève* mentioned above. All are elegant, handsome, aristocratic faces. One suspects that the artist proceeded in his portraits with a preconceived ideal in mind as to how his patrons should appear. The implications are that the court portraitist was required to work within certain restrictions as to facial type and pose.

The elongation of the form in a vertical direction is an idiosyncrasy of the Mannerist style then in vogue. At the same time elongation had been a convention in the portrayal of the French aristocracy from the time of the early fifteenth century International style.

1. Anthony Blunt, *Art and Architecture in France, 1500-1700,* Harmondsworth, Middlesex, 1973, p. 119.
2. *Ibid.*

36. School of Titian ?

Italian (Venetian)

Portrait of Doge Petrus Lando, 1545

Oil on canvas. 116.8 x 99 cm. (46 x 39″) 1971.50
Inscribed upper left: "PETRVS LANDO VENETIAR. DVX MDXLV."

The person portrayed wears the official costume of a Venetian doge, chief magistrate of the city of Venice. An inscription on the painting identifies the doge as Petrus Lando, who held office from 1539 to 1545, the year of his death. The 1545 date suggests that it was commissioned to serve as a memorial.

This interesting painting appeared upon the scene quite suddenly in 1932 in the possession of a Florentine art dealer, Arturo Grassi. Arrangements for its purchase were made by the art historians W. R. Valentiner and Lionello Venturi. Both agreed that it was an important painting by the hand of Titian himself.[1]

In the most recent comment on the work, Harold Wethey considered the painting to be a "copy or modern imitation" and "of dubious quality."[2] Wethey apparently used a photograph to make his determination and did not see the original, which appears to be sixteenth century, although the paint surface may have been extensively reworked.

However, an attribution to Titian appears to be unlikely on compositional and stylistic grounds. Titian always posed his figures in more foreshortened positions, and the brushwork is quite clumsy in the face and hands. While the drapery passages show more of Titian's style, in official portraits his drapery was never as broadly rendered as this.

It has also been observed that the portrait might not be of Petrus Lando at all.[3] Though Lionello Venturi notes that Titian painted Doge Lando three times,[4] none of these portraits can be identified. At the same time the face in the Hyde portrait seems similar to that of the Doge Andrea Gritti in the universally accepted painting by Titian in the National Gallery of Art, Washington, D.C.

1. Letters and certificates from Valentiner and Venturi, Paris, July 28, 1932.
2. Harold E. Wethey, *The Paintings of Titian,* London, 1971, II, p. 172, no. X-69.
3. Observation by Eleanor M. Hight, Harvard University.
4. Lionello Venturi, *Italian Paintings in America,* New York, 1933, III. Text with pl. 519.

Provenance: Senator Count Cittadella; Arturo Grassi; purchased from Arturo Grassi, Florence, July 28, 1932.

Literature: Venturi, *op. cit.;* Wethey, *op. cit.*

37. Tintoretto (Jacopo Robusti)

Italian (Venetian), 1518-1594

The Discovery of the True Cross, c. 1560-70

Oil on canvas. 21.3 x 48.55 cm. (8-3/8 x 19-1/8″) 1971.48

This is one of a group of three paintings of the same size, style, and theme, representing the three principal episodes of The Legend of the True Cross. The painting, *The Embarcation of St. Helena for the Holy Land* (Victoria and Albert Museum, London), depicts the beginning of the story which ends with *The Identification of the True Cross* (The Art Institute of Chicago).[1]

The small size and long narrow proportions of these paintings could only mean that together they once formed the predella of an altarpiece which would have represented St. Helena as the principal subject. Such an altarpiece by Tintoretto does exist in the Brera Gallery, Milan. In the Brera painting the cross stands in the center, with St. Helena to the left, St. Barbara to the right, and with three other male saints and a kneeling donor. The sixty-five inch width of the base is a perfect size to accommodate the overall sixty inch length of the three small canvases. On stylistic grounds both the Brera *St. Helena* and the three proposed predella paintings can be dated 1560-70.

The Brera *St. Helena* altarpiece was originally executed for the church of St. Marcuola in Venice. Between 1728 and 1736 the church was rebuilt and redecorated in a Baroque style, suggesting a possible date for the dismantling of the altarpiece. According to Hans Tietze, the painting next appeared in Milan in the church of Sta. Croce, in 1776.[2] From there it was transferred to the Brera in 1805. The provenance of the three proposed predella paintings can only be traced to the latter part of the nineteenth century.

There are a number of variations on the story of the Legend of the True Cross. The one represented by the three paintings under consideration comes from *The Golden Legend,* a compendium of apocryphal sacred stories recorded in the thirteenth century by Jacopo da Voragine. In the version recorded by Voragine, a Jew significantly named Judas, leads Helena to the site. In the Hyde painting it is Judas who holds the cross. According to the legend, a pit was dug and three crosses were found. The True Cross was identified by touching each cross, in turn, to the body of a dead man; the True Cross brought the corpse to life.

The free, sketchy manner of brushwork in these small predella panels was commonly used by Tintoretto for smaller scaled works or for the background forms and figures of his larger paintings. The distinctive handwriting of the artist can be observed in this brushwork, particularly in the peculiar zig-zag stroke with which he characteristically rendered sleeves and the open, angular lines by which his drapery forms were produced.

The Victoria and Albert Museum attributes their *Embarcation of St. Helena* to the Venetian artist Andrea Schiavone. There is a superficial resemblance to Schiavone's style (Schiavone had influenced Tintoretto), but Schiavone did not compose, as did Tintoretto, with the strong curve and counter-curve of figures which appears in the small St. Helena panels. Tintoretto invariably renders his drapery with a more curvilinear stroke. The Art Institute of Chicago now places their *Embarcation* in the workshop of Tintoretto, with a tentative attribution to the so-called "Master of the Corsini Adultress."[3]

The authenticity of the work was attested to by R. Langton Douglas,[4] W. R. Valentiner,[5] and Daniel Catton Rich,[6] but the most significant observations were made by Detlev von Hadeln when he described the drawing, modeling, and color as entirely characteristic of Tintoretto's style.[7]

1. Observation by Kathleen Arthur.
2. Hans Tietz, *Tintoretto, The Paintings and Drawings,* New York, 1948, p. 355, fig. 89.
3. Letter from J. Patrice Marandel, Curator of Earlier Painting, The Art Institute of Chicago.
4. Letter from R. Langton Douglas, London, February 5, 1935.
5. William R. Valentiner, *Illustrated Catalogue of the Rita Lydig Collection,* New York, 1913, no. 129, illustrated.
6. Letter from Daniel Catton Rich, The Art Institute of Chicago, December 16, 1940.
7. Kaiser-Friedrich Museums verein, exhibit catalogue, July-August, 1925, no. 399A. Entry by Detlev von Hadeln.

Provenance: Sir Thomas Andros de la Rue; R. Langton Douglas; Rita Lydig; F. Hess; Julius Boehler.

Literature: Valentiner, *op. cit.;* von Hadeln, *op. cit.;* Paul Cassirer, *Die Sammlung H.,* Berlin, *Gemälde Alter und Moderner Meister/Moderne Plastik,* Berlin and Luzern, 1931, no. 3, pl. III; Burton B. Fredericksen and Federico Zeri, *Census of Pre-Nineteenth Century Italian Paintings in North American Public Collections,* Cambridge, Mass., 1972, p. 200.

38. Tintoretto (Jacopo Robusti)

Italian (Venetian), 1518-1594

Portrait of the Doge Alvise Mocenigo (formerly *Portrait of a Venetian Nobleman*), c. 1570

Oil on canvas. 54 x 39.4 cm. (21-1/2 x 15-1/2") 1971.49

The great similarity of the pose, face and beard to Tintoretto's portrait of *Doge Alvise Mocenigo* (Accademia, Venice), suggests strongly that the Hyde portrait is of the same person.[1] The life-sized scale of the Hyde painting, with neither arms, hands, nor conspicuous costume, would make it probably not a full-dress portrait in itself, but rather the study from which the final portrait in the Accademia was executed. The Accademia painting can be dated with certainty between 1570-77. In these years Alvise Mocenigo served as doge. On stylistic grounds Joseph Dodge dated the Hyde work c. 1570.[2]

The Hyde portrait probably also served as the model for Mocenigo's face in the monumental but extremely reworked *Doge Alvise Mocenigo in Prayer Before the Redeemer with Members of His Family* (Sala del Consiglio, Doge's Palace, Venice); for the study for this painting in the Metropolitan Museum of Art, New York; and possibly for one or both of the portraits of Mocenigo in the Berlin-Dahlem Museum, and the National Gallery of Art, Washington, D.C.

Typical of Tintoretto's portrait style, the image does not appear to be as explicit a portrayal of an individual as one might find in the earlier Renaissance period. Instead, here naturalism has been tempered by an impulse toward abstraction, a characteristic of the Mannerist style of the time. There is present in this portrait some of the vertical elongation that is one of Mannerism's conspicuous stylistic traits. Another Mannerist portrait in The Hyde Collection, painted in France and attributed to Corneille de Lyon, is surprisingly similar in effect (number 35).

In this style which turns its back on the mastery of nature achieved in the Renaissance, anatomical elements are not clearly expressed. It is a characteristic of Tintoretto's own style to give the eyes an almost medieval emphasis, implying an inner spiritual presence. A concentrated light brings the form forward from a dark background. Thus the mystery and drama inherent in light and dark contrasts are enlisted in the service of achieving this spiritual effect. It is this handling of light and dark in Tintoretto's style that anticipates what was to become common in later Baroque art, as in Rembrandt's *Portrait of Christ* (number 51) in The Hyde Collection. Both Tintoretto and Rembrandt reflect in their art the return to spiritual values promulgated equally by the Counter Reformation movement within the Roman Church and by the Protestant reaction. But Tintoretto was one of the first to successfully express this new spirituality, and we are reminded once again of the Venetian foundation that underlies Baroque art.

1. The Accademia portrait is illustrated in Hans Tietze, *Tintoretto,* New York, 1948, p. 158.
2. Joseph Dodge, "Portrait of a Venetian Nobleman, by Tintoretto," *Art Quarterly,* VII, Summer 1944, p. 230, illustrated, p. 228.

Provenance: Collection of Sir Claude Alexander, 2nd Baronet of Ballochmyle House, Mauchline, Ayrshire, Scotland, prior to 1940; purchased from Lilienfeld Galleries, New York, 1943.

Literature: Dodge, *op. cit.*

39. Paolo Veronese

Italian (Venetian), 1528-1588

Rebecca at the Well, c. 1570-80

Oil on canvas. 47 x 56 cm. (18-1/2 x 22″) 1971.57

The historical subject of this painting, Rebecca putting on a bracelet which had been given to her by the servant of Abraham, is recorded in Genesis XXIV. The event occurred in Mesopotamia where the servant had been sent to seek a wife for Abraham's son, Isaac. Somewhat before this episode the servant, while in prayer, had made arrangements with God to devise a sign by which an appropriate wife for Isaac might be identified. "And let it come to pass, that the damsel to whom I shall say, 'Let down thy pitcher, I pray thee, that I may drink;' and she shall say, 'Drink, and I will give thy camels drink also:' let the same be she that thou hast appointed for thy servant Isaac." (Genesis XXIV, 14.)

In the painting Rebecca is depicted at the point where she had just finished watering the camels, and to her surprise has received from this total stranger "a golden earring of half a shekel weight, and two bracelets for her hands of ten shekels weight of gold." (Genesis XXIV, 22.) Since this arrangement of jewelry is reversed in the painting, Veronese did not accurately follow the story. Rebecca has put on *two* earrings and a *single* bracelet. The servant of Abraham seems to have been misinterpreted by the artist as a shepherd with his staff and accompanying sheep. The second servant opening the jewel casket, and the male figure drawing water from the well, are both absent from the Biblical account. In another version of this subject by Veronese (National Gallery of Art, Washington, D.C.), the male figure at the well does not appear, though the second servant is present. In the Washington version the second servant kneels and hands Abraham's servant a bracelet with his left hand, while with his right hand he grasps a box of jewels. The gesture of Abraham's servant is quite similar to that in the Hyde painting. His left hand holds a staff, while his right hand reaches for the bracelet. Similar also are the gestures of the two Rebeccas, with the right hand touching the bracelet on the left wrist. For these similarities the two works are clearly related, though the Washington version is much larger (57-1/4 x 111-1/4″). Related also is Veronese's *Rebecca at the Well* (collection of Earl of Yarborough), though the principal figures are reversed.

The attribution of this painting to Veronese seems to be reasonably certain, not only for its similarity to the other versions, but also for the fact that the figure of Rebecca is quite characteristic of Veronese's style. The rich colors and the general rendering of the figures on the right suggest the style of Veronese's Venetian contemporary Jacopo Bassano (1510-92), but this may be explained by the fact that Veronese was influenced by Bassano after 1570. It is this Bassano influence that helps to establish the date of the painting.

Provenance: Collection of Charles Alexandre de Calonne?, March 3, 1795; purchased from Lilienfeld Galleries, New York, 1948.

Literature: Skinner and Dyck, *Catalogue . . . of Valuable Pictures, the Property of the Right Hon. Charles Alexander De Calonne . . .* London, 1745, no. 62; William Buchanan, *Memoirs of Painting,* London, 1824, I, p. 238, no. 62; Algernon Graves, *Art Sales from Early in the Eighteenth Century to Early in the Twentieth Century,* London, 1918-21, III, p. 301.

40. Hans Bol

Flemish, 1534-1593

Valley of the Meuse with Apollo and Daphne, 1578

Oil or gouache on canvas. 46 x 74 cm. (18-1/8 x 29-1/8″) 1971.9
Signed and dated at bottom, left of center: "HANS BOL 1578."

In this painting of 1578 one stands at the threshold of the development of landscape painting as an independent art form. The story element of Apollo in pursuit of Daphne is reduced to a minor note, while nature itself becomes the principal actor in the scene. The work bears the title *Valley of the Meuse* possibly because the steep escarpments resemble somewhat the topography of the valley of the Meuse River that passes into Belgium from Northern France. At the same time the view may simply reflect a tradition in landscape arrangement that originated in the early fifteenth century. The characteristics of this tradition are the high horizon, winding river leading into the distance, and the steep cliffs. A famous example of such a landscape setting is the background of Leonardo da Vinci's *Mona Lisa* (Louvre, Paris). Such settings appear in the paintings of earlier Italian artists, but they most likely originated in Northern European art, in the early fifteenth century International Style. Prototypes for such craggy-river settings may be found as early as 1394-99 in the background of Melchior Broederlam's *Presentation and Flight into Egypt* (Musée des Beaux-Arts, Dijon). Slightly later one sees a similar setting in Robert Campin's *Dijon Nativity* (Musée de la Ville, Dijon), c. 1420, though in this instance the winding pathway into space becomes a road.

The artist Joachim Patinir, usually considered to be the first specialist in landscape painting, actually came from one of the towns of the Meuse Valley, and its topography inspired his characteristic scenes where, as in Bol's work in The Hyde Collection, a river flanked by cliffs recedes to a high, distant horizon. Patinir's landscapes lead directly to Bol, but the landscapes of Pieter Brueghel must have given the final form to Bol's style. From such paintings as Brueghel's *Return of the Herd,* 1565 (Kunsthistorisches Museum, Vienna), Bol derived the sense of nature's immensity that is such a striking aspect of his painting in The Hyde Collection.

Bol's problem was that, naively, he tried to include perhaps too much. On the far left Daphne is saved from Apollo by the magic intervention of her father, the river god Peneus, who transforms his daughter into a Laurel tree. Both figures are chastely clad, Daphne in classical garb, Apollo in a hunting costume. On the right the architectural components of a medieval town are romantically represented. The human and animal activity occurring throughout the scene is extraordinary for its sheer quantity and variety.

An apparent companion piece for this work is in the Los Angeles County Museum of Art. The same size and date, it includes what appears to be a view of the river Scheldt near the city of Antwerp.[1] Hans Bol arrived in Antwerp in 1572, a refugee from his native city of Malines. It was in 1572 that Malines was sacked by a Spanish army under the Duke of Alva. Although the Los Angeles painting contains no mythological subject, the many couples strolling hand in hand, and in one instance making love, suggest that the two paintings together had love as their common theme.

Bol was born in Malines in 1534. A student of two of his uncles, he spent the early part of his career in Heidelburg, Germany, in the employ of the Elector of the Palatinate. Later he returned to Malines and worked there until the sack of 1572. In 1584 he left Antwerp for Holland, where he resided first in Bergen op Zoom, then in Dordrecht, then Delft, and finally settled in Amsterdam. Bol had a great influence on the development of Dutch landscape painting. One sees a reflection of his style in the landscapes of Hercules Seghers, who in turn influenced Rembrandt. Bol died in Amsterdam in 1593.

While the *Valley of the Meuse* appears to have been executed in oil, it has been suggested by conservators that it may be a water-soluble medium such as gouache.

1. Wolfgang Stechow, *Dutch Landscape Painting in the Seventeenth Century,* London, 1966, p. 33.

Provenance: Purchased from John Mitchell, Fine Paintings, New York, 1946.

41. Anonymous

Flemish

Allegory of Spring with Flora, Vertumnus, and Pomona, c. 1600

Tapestry, wool. 218.4 x 226.1 cm. (86 x 89") 1971.118

In the center of this tapestry, an apparently aging gardener is in consultation with the Roman goddesses Flora and Pomona. Flora, who can be identified by her floral crown, was the goddess of the spring season, while Pomona, with her identifying crown of grape clusters, was the goddess of orchards, vineyards, and fruit-bearing trees. Together they and the flowering garden represent springtime. It has been suggested that this tapestry may have been one of a group of four representing the four seasons, a subject of great popularity in Northern European decorative arts.[1]

The gardener might also be interpreted as Vertumnus, the Roman god, protector of gardens and orchards, who had disguised himself as an old gardener in an attempt to approach the virginal Pomona who, according to the ancient legend in Ovid's *Metamorphoses,* avoided all men. This interpretation can be further supported by the popularity of the Vertumnus and Pomona legend, which was a common subject in Flemish tapestries during the sixteenth and early seventeenth centuries.

The appearance of the garden theme itself in the visual arts, was derived from the love gardens of late medieval poetry. Settings for the pursuit of courtly love, these love gardens were laden with connotations of chaste and unchaste love, as well as of fertility. In the Hyde tapestry these meanings are reinforced by the presence of Vertumnus, who represents passion, the chaste Pomona, and Flora, who as the goddess of fertility represents unchaste love. In a tradition dating back to the fifteenth century in European art, the love garden often appeared in art works commissioned to commemorate marriages, a relationship which should not be overlooked in its possible connection to this and the many other tapestries illustrating the Vertumnus and Pomona theme from this period.

The name of the weaver and the designer of this tapestry would have appeared on borders which are now missing. It seems likely that it was woven in Flanders because at that time the Flemish monopolized the art of weaving, executing designs received from artists throughout Europe. The high horizon and the dramatic receding perspective are characteristic of late Mannerist compositions, suggesting a possible date for the work of around 1600.

1. Entry by Jane Rehl.

42. Domenico Theotocopuli, called El Greco

Spanish (born in Crete), 1541-1614

Portrait of St. James the Less, c. 1610-15

Oil on canvas. 62.9 x 50.2 cm. (24-3/4 x 19-3/4") 1971.18

St. James the Less comes from a series of portraits of Christ's followers by El Greco known as the Henke Apostles, since in the last century they formed a part of the Henke Collection in Seville, Spain. Whether this series is from the artist's own hand or a production of his assistants, is a question that has been raised by Harold Wethey in his catalogue raisonné of El Greco's work.[1]

The identification of the saint is more by a process of elimination than anything else, since he holds no attributes. Some years ago the scholar Walter Cook and others speculated that the face portrayed may be a self-portrait of the artist.[2]

Such half-length portraits of saints were popular at the time, possibly because of the tremendous revival of interest in saints due to the Counter Reformation movement. The subject originated in the icon painting of Italy and Greece of the Middle Ages, but in this period the darkness of the real world has replaced the shining gold-leaf backgrounds of traditional icons, which stood for the light of God.

The painting, coming as it does near the end of the artist's career, shows his spiritualization of form at its greatest extreme. The thin face of the saint reflects a Christian ideal of asceticism. Neither brushstroke nor modeling creates a clear-cut, solid form, but the paint flows over the form with a suggestion of flame-like flickering, while glowing colors and extensive glazing of the surface produce an effect like stained glass.

1. Harold Wethey, *El Greco and His School, Catalogue Raisonné,* Princeton, 1962, II, p. 212.
2. Walter W. S. Cook, letter dated November 4, 1949, Hyde Archives.

Provenance: History of Henke Apostles as traced by Harold Wethey, *op. cit.:* probably Convento de Las Baronesas, Madrid, eighteenth century; collection of López Cepero y Cañaveral, Seville, 1843; collection of Don Alberto Henke, Seville, 1900-1930; private collection, Germany, 1931. (Walter Cook, in a letter in the Hyde Archives, says the "entire Henke Collection from Seville" was acquired by a New York art dealer named Frederick Mont.) Wethey places them in the Seligman Galleries, New York, 1934; purchased from Lilienfeld Galleries, New York, 1949.

Literature: Manuel B. Cossio, *El Greco,* Madrid, 1908, p. 580, no. 171; August L. Mayer, *El Greco,* Munich, 1926, p. 23, no. 147; August L. Mayer, *El Greco,* Berlin, 1931, p. 85; José Camón Aznar, *Domenico Greco,* Madrid, 1950, no. 333, illustrated p. 1403; Harold Wethey, *op. cit.,* p. 212, no. X223.

43. Peter Paul Rubens

Flemish, 1577-1640

Man in Armor, c. 1615

Oil on wooden panel. 49.5 x 40.9 cm. (19-1/2 x 16-1/8″) 1971.41

The hunched position of the body and the side-long brooding glance of the shadowed eyes, suggest this is not a portrait. Instead, the sitter here is an actor in his role, consistent with the central purpose of Baroque art. The bearded figure, dressed in armor and a cloak, was the standard hero type for Rubens. Examples appear in two paintings in Munich in the Alte-Pinakothek, executed by Rubens close in time to the Hyde work under consideration; *The Hero Crowned by Victory* and *Triumph of the Victor.* The small format of the Hyde painting suggests that the image was to serve as the model for a head in a larger work, as was the Hyde's *Head of a Negro* (number 44), though neither appears in any extant composition by the artist.

The date of 1610-12 ascribed to this work by Julius Held, may be too early to account for the fluid breadth of the artist's fully mature style, which is quite evident here.[1] During these years some of the hardness of the artist's early manner still persists. The date of 1615 given by Jo-seph Dodge appears to be more correct.[2] It is the date also given by W. R. Valentiner in his certificate of authenticity.[3] The Lilienfeld Galleries, New York dated the work even later, 1618-20, when they presented it for sale in 1941.

A larger replica of this painting, in which a right arm and hand appear, poses certain problems. Although it was discussed in an article by Ludwig Burchard when it was in a private collection, the painting does not seem to have been scrutinized by any Rubens' scholar since, and its present location is apparently unknown. Burchard placed the work in Rubens' Italian period before 1608, possibly to account for weaknesses in the style which are visible in even a bad reproduction. Dodge, working from a good photograph, concluded that it was a copy.[4] The clumsiness of the added arm and hand suggest that it was a contrivance by someone other than Rubens.

It should be noted that the proportions of the Hyde work were altered at some later date by the addition of a one-inch-wide vertical strip along the left border.

1. Jan-Albert Goris and Julius Held, *Rubens in America,* New York, 1947, p. 30, no. 22.
2. Joseph Dodge, "Rubens 'Man in Armor'," *The Art Quarterly,* V, Spring, 1942, p. 187.
3. W. R. Valentiner's endorsement on photo, the Hyde Archives, December 2, 1940.
4. Dodge, *op. cit.,* p. 188.

Provenance: Purchased from art dealer Donjeu (incorrectly Dongen or van Dongen in other sources) by Henry Temple, second Viscount Palmerston (father of the British prime minister), Paris, 1791; remained at Broadlands, near Ramsey, Hampshire with Temple family through Lady Edwina Cynthia Annette Mount Temple (wife of famous W.W. II British military leader, Louis Mountbatten) until 1940; purchased from Lilienfeld Galleries, New York, 1941.

Literature: John Smith, *A Catalogue Raisonné of the Works of the Most Eminent Dutch, Flemish, and French Painters,* London, 1830, II, *Peter Paul Rubens,* p. 309, no. 1135; Royal Academy of Arts, London, *17th Century, Art in Europe,* no. 104; Schaeffer and Brandt, Inc., *Peter Paul Rubens,* November 23-December 19, 1942, no. 6, illustrated; Joseph Dodge, *op. cit.;* Jan-Albert Goris and Julius Held, *op. cit.,* p. 30, no. 22, pl. VI; S. Lane Faison, Jr., *Art Tours and Detours in New York State,* New York, 1964. pp. 113-114.

Exhibitions: Royal Academy of Arts, London, 1871, no. 71, Royal Academy of Arts, London, *17th Century Art in Europe,* 1938; Fogg Art Museum, Cambridge, Mass., October 1941; Shaeffer and Brandt, Inc., New York, *Peter Paul Rubens,* November 23-December 19, 1942.

44. Peter Paul Rubens

Flemish, 1577-1640

Head of a Negro, c. 1620

Oil on wooden panel. 45.6 x 36.8 cm. (18 x 14-1/2″) 1971.40

A study taken from life to be duplicated at a later time in a large composition, this is a typical *modello* by Rubens. Such studies, broadly painted and direct in every sense, show the full genius of Rubens' art.

The same model appears in a study of four heads now in the Royal Museum, Brussels. Although the attribution of this work has shifted from van Dyck to Rubens and back again, presently the weight of opinion ascribes the painting to Rubens. A variation on the Brussels study is in the J. Paul Getty Museum, Malibu, California, but its attribution has been questioned by Julius Held.[1]

The differences between the Hyde and Brussels studies are significant. In the Hyde sketch the brushwork is broader and there is greater intensity and variety of color. Since Rubens' style became progressively broader as it evolved, this may indicate a later date for the Hyde work.[2]

The Brussels painting records the model reacting naturally and spontaneously, while in the Hyde work, he was required to assume a reverent expression. Clearly the latter was to be a study for the black king in the subject of the Adoration of the Kings. The black king appears occasionally as far back as the twelfth century in European art, to represent the continent Africa paying homage to the new born Christ.[3] In Flemish art he makes his appearance at least as early as 1472 in Hugo van der Goes' *Montforte Altarpiece* (Berlin-Dahlem, Staatliche Museum). Since that time the black king was a constant in the Magi theme in Flemish art, and in the art of such countries as Germany, where Flemish influence was strong.

Almost invariably the black king is portrayed as standing, and rarely does he appear to be moved to reverence, as in the Hyde *Adoration of the Kings,* Antwerp School (number 32) or in Rubens' own *Adoration* of 1624 (Musée Royal des Beaux-Arts, Antwerp). The pose in the Hyde work suggests that it may have been for a kneeling king, possibly even the principal king who kneels directly before Christ and his mother. Such a radical departure from traditional representations of the black king probably accounts for the fact that this *modello* was never used in any extant painting by Rubens.

The Hyde painting was executed on a wooden panel, the paint being applied to a light-colored ground which had been scored with thin parallel lines, as if made by a comb. Such scoring appears in the Hyde *Man in Armor* and is common in Rubens' paintings on panel.

The condition of the painting is excellent with no indication of any later retouching.

1. Julius Held, "Four Heads of a Negro in Brussels and Malibu," *Bulletin de l'Institute Royal du Patrimoine Artistique,* 1975, XV, pp. 180-192.
2. Held dates the Hyde work c. 1618-20, the Brussels version 1613-15. Julius Held, *The Oil Sketches of Peter Paul Rubens,* Princeton, 1980, p. 612.
3. cf. above, number 32, for a discussion of the Adoration of the Kings.

Provenance: Count Schwanenberg?; purchased from Lilienfeld Galleries, New York, 1938.

Literature: George Henry McCall and William R. Valentiner, *Masterpieces of Art, New York World's Fair, 1939, Catalogue of European Painting and Sculpture from 1300-1800,* New York, 1939, p. 162, no. 331; Jan-Albert Goris and Julius S. Held, *Rubens in America,* New York, 1947, p. 30, no. 30, pl. 7; Van Diemen, Lilienfeld Galleries, New York, *Masterpieces of Five Centuries* (commemorating the diamond jubilee of the Philadelphia Museum of Art), January 20-February 3, 1951, no. 15; Museum Boymans-Van Beuningen, *Olieverfschetsen van Rubens,* Rotterdam, 1953, p. 48, no. 17; Fogg Art Museum, Cambridge, Mass. and the Morgan Library, New York, *Drawings and Watercolors from American Collections,* 1956, p. 32, no. 36, pl. XXIII; S. Lane Faison, Jr., *Art Tours and Detours in New York State,* New York, 1964, p. 110, fig. 189, p. 113; Michael Jaffé, *Bulletin of the National Gallery of Canada,* XII, 1969, p. 9; Held, *The Oil Sketches of Peter Paul Rubens, op. cit.,* p. 612, no. 447, pl. 435.

Exhibitions: Masterpieces of Art, New York World's Fair, 1939, no. 331; The Fogg Art Museum, Cambridge, Mass., October 1941; Van Dieman-Lilienfeld Galleries, New York, January 20-February 3, 1951; Fogg Art Museum, Cambridge, Mass., January 14-February 29, 1956; The Morgan Library, New York, March 20-April 28, 1956.

45. Circle of Frans Hals

Dutch

So-called *Portrait of the Artist's Son,* c. 1630

Oil on oval wooden panel. 19.7 x 16.5 cm. (7-3/4 x 6-1/2″) 1971.21
Signed in monogram, lower right: "F.H."

Frans Hals was one of the great portraitists of seventeenth century Holland, but the Hyde painting is not commensurate with the quality of this artist's work. In his certificate of authenticity, W. R. Valentiner related this painting to three small portraits of a similar nature attributed to Hals.[1] All three of these have recently been rejected by Seymour Slive.[2] (*Portrait of a Girl,* now in the possession of Mr. and Mrs. Herrington, Indianapolis, and two portraits of a boy in the Philadelphia Museum of Art, John G. Johnson Collection, Philadelphia, Slive nos. D. 67, D. 41, and D. 42.)

There is almost no precedent among Hals' authentic work of such a complete profile view, nor is the brushwork as clear or as vivid as it would be in Hals' characteristic style, particularly around the eyes and mouth.

Among Hals' works, portraits of this type fall into the category of genre paintings. Representing intriguing, often low-life human subjects, these portraits may have been done for the artist's own pleasure or for the Dutch art market. The roguish young man in a fancy hat is a common theme among Hals' genre portraits of the 1620's. Almost always the subject is represented with vanitas symbols — a wine glass, skull, or musical instrument, and these represent, quite simply, human folly. The absence of such symbols is perhaps indicative of the fact that the artist of this work was unaware of Hals' original purpose.

1. Letter from W. R. Valentiner, the Hyde Archives, Detroit, March 15, 1940.
2. Seymour Slive, *Frans Hals,* London and New York, 1970, pp. 151, 143.

Provenance: Sir Claude Alexander, Bart., Ballochmyle House, Mauchline, Scotland; Miss Anne Huskisson, Edinbridge, Kent, England; purchased from Lilienfeld Galleries, New York, March 15, 1940.

46. Pieter Neeffs, the Elder ?

Flemish (Antwerp), c. 1578-c. 1659

Interior of a Gothic Church, c. 1625-50

Oil on wooden panel. 23.5 x 29.8 cm. (9-1/4 x 11-3/4") 1971.31
Inscribed on paper on back: "Bought at Christi 1756."
Inscribed upside down on the panel: "Hendrik van Balen."

Church interiors first appeared in North European art as settings for sacred themes in the paintings of the great Flemish master of the early fifteenth century, Jan van Eyck. By the seventeenth century they had become secularized. Divested of their sacred meanings, the interior space itself became the subject. Religious activity is absent among the human forms that move through this space. While these church visitors are dressed in seventeenth century costume, the church itself is in the Gothic architectural style of an earlier time. The question must be raised, why such a subject? The fact that a number of artists could specialize in it indicates it must have been a popular product in the art market of the time. The simplest answer could be that, like the cityscapes, landscapes, and seascapes of the time, the subject of church interiors was developed in response to the general Netherlandish passion to see its world reflected in, and therefore exalted by, art. A middle class finds its greatest aesthetic interest in itself. But in perhaps half the cases these Flemish church interiors cannot be recognized. They are imaginary creations, and therefore have a purer aesthetic value than would the transcription of familiar places.

At the same time architectural interiors would provide the artist with the opportunity to develop an elaborate perspective scheme, and therefore to create extraordinary illusions of space on the flat surface of the picture. To the seventeenth century mind, such illusions possessed all the fascination of magic transformation, and were exciting for their own sake.

The attribution of this painting to the Flemish artist Pieter Neeffs the Elder is by no means certain. The style may be too clumsy for Neeffs himself, although the work certainly reflects Neeffs' direct influence. One can be reasonably certain that it was painted in the Catholic city of Antwerp sometime between 1625-50. The church interior subject had been developed somewhat earlier by the artist Hendrik van Steenwyck the Elder. It was transmitted to the Neeffs, father and son, by Hendrik van Steenwyck the Younger. The name of the Antwerp artist, Hendrik van Balen (1560-1638), is inscribed upside down on the back of the panel. Van Balen's style and historical subject matter would be very different from this work. Possibly he was once its owner.

Provenance: Purchased from Mortimer Brandt Galleries, New York, 1950.

47. Pieter de Molijn

Dutch, 1594-1661

Landscape, 1626

Black chalk on paper. 18.7 x 28.6 cm. (7-3/8 x 11-1/4") 1971.75
Signed lower center: "P. Molyn."

This drawing is closely related to Molijn's painting, *Landscape with a Sandy Road* (Herzog Anton Ulrich Museum, Braunschweig, Germany). Wolfgang Stechow believed it to be the artist's major work and one of the pivotal paintings in the development of the art of landscape in Holland.[1] The importance of this painting and the Hyde drawing is that they are landscapes of a more direct and simple type than had been seen before in art history. The view lacks conspicuous human figures or anecdotal subject matter. It also represents a direct break with the tradition of dramatic landscape which, in North European art, goes back through Brueghel to Patinir and Altdorfer. The view of nature is close, intimate, and quite normal. Not again until the Barbizon School in the nineteenth century is nature so simply portrayed.

While the overall composition of a diagonal road leading in, counter-balanced by a diagonal tree, goes back to the German artist Adam Elsheimer, who might be the immediate source of Baroque landscape painting, the close unity of surface is new and anticipates developments which will occur in the landscape style of Jan van Goyen. Contrasts of light and shade are reduced and a relatively even tonal quality spreads throughout the surface. Objec-tive rendering of the parts, normal in the Dutch style before this, gives way before the texture of the draftsmanship, a technique that van Goyen will carry further. According to Stechow, after the spectacular innovations of the Braunschweig painting, also present in the Hyde drawing, Molijn followed rather than led. His painting of 1657 of figures and horses in the Rijksmuseum, Amsterdam, indicates that in his later style he returned again to an anecdotal subject matter.

Pieter de Molijn was born in London and died in the Dutch city of Haarlem. It seems likely that he was a student of the portraitist Frans Hals since he appears in a famous group portrait of the artists who worked in Hals' studio. Molijn achieved the position of master painter in the city of Haarlem in 1616.

Molijn belongs to the generation of Dutch landscape painters that includes Jan van Goyen, Salomon van Ruysdael, and Esajas van de Velde.

Little is known about Pieter de Molijn and his works are rare, but the painting in Braunschweig and the Hyde drawing clearly establish his importance in the history of art.

1. Wolfgang Stechow, *Dutch Landscape Painting,* London, 1966, pp. 23-24.

Provenance: Purchased from Dr. R. Mermod of Lausanne, Switzerland in 1929. In a note copied in the Hyde Archives, Dr. R. Mermod writes that it, and a drawing by Watteau "are out of the collection of the Baron de Stuess." Later correspondence indicates the Watteau was not found to be authentic, and the original owner had "left for foreign parts, address unknown."

48. Anthony van Dyck

Flemish, 1599-1641

Portrait of Jan Woverius (Jan van den Wouwere; Jean Wouverius), c. 1634

Oil on canvas. 45.7 x 31.7 cm. (18 x 12-1/2″) 1971.52

This portrait, in a long-standing Flemish tradition, represents the sitter against a dark background. Typical of van Dyck is the restrained and aristocratic presentation, devoid of deep personality and of emotion. It is a style eminently suited to the official portraiture upon which van Dyck's fame as an artist rests.

The sitter Jan Woverius can be identified from an etching dated 1632 by Paulus Pontius (1603-1658) of Woverius in the same pose. The print formed part of van Dyck's *Icones principum. . . .* of 1646, a series of etched portraits of the famous men of his day.

Jan Woverius (1576-1635) was a classical scholar turned politician and diplomat. In 1614 he was an alderman in Antwerp. Later under Albert and Isabella in Brussels, he was Minister of Finance, serving also as Isabella's trusted financial agent. The most interesting fact about Woverius was that he was one of Peter Paul Rubens' closest friends. In a famous group portrait, *Four Philosophers,* 1611-12 (Pitti Palace, Florence), Rubens portrayed Jan Woverius, his brother Philip Rubens and their tutor Justus Lipsius of Louvain. Rubens himself appears slightly behind the group and to the left.

A number of replicas exist of this portrait of Woverius. The most noted is the large, half-length portrait in the Pushkin Museum, Moscow.[1] Of the Hyde portrait, Max Rooses says, "My opinion is that the portrait was painted by Anthony van Dyck, probably in 1634."[2] Rooses observed that some slight retouching of the face had occurred. W. R. Valentiner described the portrait as a "workshop replica."[3] Replicas of the master's original work were commonly produced by van Dyck's assistants.

The size, format, and quality of this work suggest that it either is, or duplicates, the original *modello* taken by van Dyck from life. From such *modelli,* more official portraits of a larger scale were produced, such as the version of this painting in Moscow.

The date of 1634, given by Rooses for the Hyde portrait, would place it during van Dyck's brief return to Flanders from England, 1634-35.

1. Erik Larsen, *L'Opera Completa di Van Dyck,* Milan, 1980, p. 106, illustrated.
2. Letter from Max Rooses, Antwerp, May 16, 1911.
3. Letter from W. R. Valentiner, August 1, 1932.

Provenance: Purchased from Percy Moore Turner, London through the E. and A. Milch Galleries, Inc., New York, 1930.

Literature: Larsen, *op. cit.,* no. 734, illustrated.

49. Rembrandt Harmenszoon van Rijn

Dutch, 1606-1669

Portrait of the Artist's Mother [Neeltgen (Cornelia) Willemsdochter van Zuytbroeck], 1631

Etching on paper. 9.5 x 7 cm. (3-3/4 x 2-3/4") 1971.83
Signed and dated on the plate at bottom: "RL·1631."
Second state of seven, Bartsch 349; Hind 50.

In this small etching, utter realism, one of the most striking aspects of Rembrandt's personal style, is apparent. Never has an artist's mother appeared more mortal or more unattractive. Mortality, the action of passing time on flesh, is a central theme in Rembrandt's art. It is probable that this was as much a conscious choice on Rembrandt's part as it was an instinctive predilection. In the intellectual circles of Leyden which were strongly Calvinistic, mortality, the transitoriness of human life, was a popular philosophical concern.

In a portrait of the artist's aging mother, one would expect even from Rembrandt some improvement over true appearances. However, he actually seemed to revel in her multitude of wrinkles and bulging facial features. Rembrandt's portraits of his mother are never sentimental, but quite the reverse. The artist loved her very much, but one never senses in her expression any motherly tenderness or love of the sort that he introduced so convincingly into the face of the mother of Jesus. Age had erected a dense mask before his mother's inner self, and it is that mask only that the artist allows us to see.

Signed "R.L.," Rembrandt's abbreviation for "Rembrandt Leidensis" (Rembrandt of Leyden), and dated 1631, this etching must have been executed shortly before the artist left Leyden, the city of his birth, for Amsterdam. Rembrandt portrayed his mother a number of times, both in portraits and in his story paintings. With two exceptions, all of these portrayals belong to his early Leyden years. The first exception is a small etched portrait dated 1633; the second, the great last portrait of his mother of 1639, which was executed the year before her death (Kunsthistorisches Museum, Vienna).

It was in 1589 that Cornelia van Zuytbroeck married Harmen Gerritszoon, Rembrandt's father. How they came together is clear enough, since Harmen was a miller and Cornelia's father was a baker. Harmen's mill stood beside a northern branch of the Rhine River. For that reason, it was called van Rijn, the source of the "van Rijn" that Harmen added to his name. Cornelia bore nine children of which seven lived. Rembrandt was the eighth child. Although the date for Cornelia's birth cannot be found, judging from the date of her marriage, 1589, she would have been around sixty at the time of the Hyde etching.

Rembrandt's father had died in 1630. In 1631 Rembrandt purchased a house in Leyden, but a series of artistic commissions persuaded him to move to Amsterdam before the end of the year. In Amsterdam he lived with the art dealer Hendrik van Uylenburgh, uncle of his future wife Saskia. It was not until 1639 that he purchased his own house in Amsterdam. It must have been in that year that he was joined by his mother. In 1640 she died.

Provenance: Purchased from Kennedy and Company, New York, 1929.

Literature: (the references are to other impressions) Adam Bartsch ed., *Catalogue Raisonné de Toutes les Estampes qui Forment L'Oeuvre de Rembrandt* . . . Vienna, 1797, and later eds., no. 349; Arthur M. Hind, *A Catalogue of Rembrandt's Etching,* New York, reprint of the 2nd ed., 1923 London, p. 92, no. 50, illustrated. In publications of the complete etchings of Rembrandt by Schild (1937), Boon (1963), and Harris (1970). Illustrated in each case.

50. Rembrandt Harmenszoon van Rijn

Dutch, 1606-1669

Two Men Shaking Hands, c. 1635

Pen and ink on paper. 14.6 x 12 cm. (5-3/4 x 4-3/4″) 1971.78

Unrelated to any extant work by Rembrandt, the subject of this drawing cannot be securely identified. W. R. Valentiner felt that it represented the story of Eli and Elkanah (I Samuel, II, 20), which begins, "And Eli blessed Elkanah and his wife."[1] However, since the presence of Elkanah's wife, Hannah, is not even suggested in what appears to be a complete composition, this subject seems unlikely. One has to look elsewhere, possibly to the story of Abram and Melchizedek. Melchizedek, King of Salem and high priest, may well have greeted Abram in such a manner after his victory over King Chedorlaomer of Elam (Genesis XIV, 18-19).

Rembrandt's priests of the Old Testament may be recognized by their turbanned headdresses with the fall of cloth behind. Such a headdress is worn by the priest in the *Presentation of Christ in the Temple,* 1631 (Mauritshuis, The Hague). The presence of a feather in the turban can designate royalty, as in the *David Playing the Harp Before Saul,* c. 1629 (Städelsches Kunstinstitut, Frankfurt). The horn-like stroke rising from the turbanned figure in the Hyde drawing probably indicates this feather. The same headdress appears in a close-up, detailed view in Rembrandt's etching dated 1635, entitled *The Third Oriental Head.*[2] As a compromise date, 1635 may be arrived at for the Hyde drawing. Valentiner places it between 1635-40;[3] Benesch dated the drawing 1632-33 on the basis of style.[4] The Hyde drawing was probably a preparatory study for an etching. It is related in format to certain of Rembrandt's etchings executed between 1634-1645 such as *Christ and the Woman of Samaria,* 1634;[5] *Jacob and Laban,* 1641;[6] and *Abraham and Isaac,* 1645.[7] These compositional similarities again suggest a later date than the 1632-33 given by Benesch.

Rembrandt's genius is evident in what is an astonishing characteristic of his draftsmanship in general. No matter how free the artist's pen strokes, a clear human drama is conveyed with powerful effect. The priest-king on the left obviously is speaking, his thoughts projected with the energy of an actor on a stage. The person on the right listens, but his open hand conveys the impression that he is on the brink of speaking himself; the sense of active emotional life is very great. This dramatic quality, present throughout Baroque art, is perhaps more successfully realized in the art of Rembrandt than in any other instance.

1. W. R. Valentiner, *Rembrandt's Handzeichnungen, Klassiker der Kunst,* Stuttgart, Berlin and Leipzig, n.d., II, pp. 368, 431, no. 808, illustrated.
2. Arthur M. Hind, *A Catalogue of Rembrandt's Etchings,* New York, 1967, p. 77, no. 133.
3. Valentiner, *op. cit.,* p. 368.
4. Otto Benesch, *The Drawings of Rembrandt,* London, 1954, I, p. 24, no. 75, fig. 95.
5. Hind, *op. cit.,* p. 74, no. 122.
6. *Ibid.,* p. 89, no. 183.
7. *Ibid.,* p. 96, no. 214.

Provenance: M. Kappel; W. R. Valentiner; purchased from the auction galleries of Mensing et Fils, Amsterdam, October 1932. (The purchase of this drawing from Valentiner's collection was a few months after his first professional contact with the Hydes.)

Literature: A. W. M. Mensing et Fils, *Dessins de Rembrandt, Collection W. R. Valentiner,* Amsterdam, 1932, p. 2, no. III, illustrated; Valentiner, *op. cit.;* Benesch, *op. cit.;* Milwaukee Art Institute, *Catalogue of the Inaugural Exhibition,* 1957, no. 23; S. Lane Faison, Jr., *Art Tours and Detours in New York State,* New York, 1964, p. 114, fig. 191.

Exhibitions: Milwaukee Art Institute, 1957.

51. Rembrandt Harmenszoon van Rijn

Dutch, 1606-1669

Portrait of Christ (formerly *Christ with Folded Arms*), c. 1655-57

Oil on canvas. 109.2 x 90.2 cm. (43 x 35-1/2") 1971.37

In the portrayal of this image of Christ, Rembrandt demonstrated what was his particular talent, the introduction into a human form of a number of unambiguous psychological and moral connotations. In this instance these connotations pertain to the personality of Jesus as it appears in the Bible and in Protestant theology, subtly interpreted and synthesized by Rembrandt's artistic genius. In the lines of this face we immediately discern a high nobility and a high intelligence. There is also a great potential for love and human sympathy. At the same time one encounters a sense of a pervading sadness, the sadness that is present in all of Rembrandt's later portraits. The tragedies of his own life made him perceive tragedy as an ingrained aspect of the human condition. Sadness in the face of Christ makes one conscious of his concern for mankind's miseries, as well as of his clairvoyant awareness of his own fate. One imagines that the Christ in Leonardo's *Last Supper* (Santa Maria delle Grazie, Milan), may have looked like this.

In this life-sized image Christ appears alone, surrounded by darkness. Although there is a certain ambiguity in the pose, he seems to be seated, for a curve at the lower right suggests the left side of a chair. His head and shoulders are in the exact position assumed by *Jan Six* (Six Foundation, Amsterdam), Rembrandt's famous portrait of 1654. The head is turned slightly down and toward the picture's right. His eyes are not focused on any external object. One has the certain impression that his attention is directed within his mind, a common characteristic of Rembrandt's later portraits. As if Christ were in meditation, his breath passes gently through partly opened lips. In a gesture rare in art, Christ's arms are crossed at the wrists, the left arm over the right. A point of light above the left sleeve indicates the tip of the thumb of the right hand, showing that it is held open against Christ's heart. Possibly the crossed wrists are a reference to the binding of his wrists during his Passion. But the gesture may simply refer to a receiving of the divine spirit, as at baptism.

At Christ's left an architectural pier is faintly visible. The implication may be that he is within a temple. A similar but more visible pier may be seen in Rembrandt's *Portrait of Christ* dated 1661 (Metropolitan Museum of Art, Bache Collection, New York).

Part of the illumination within the painting comes from the picture's right. At least as far back as Jan van Eyck, paintings in North European art were lighted from the picture's right as a way of indicating a divine presence. A symbolic reading of the light in Jan Vermeer's interiors indicates that this meaning was still understood in Rembrandt's time in Holland.

In the Hyde portrait Christ is himself a source of a mystical light. Thus his divine nature is magically affirmed. Rembrandt made certain that the viewer recognize Christ as being internally illuminated by the peculiar device of having light shine out from his left sleeve.

It is the divine nature of Christ that Rembrandt emphasized in this work. The crossed arms divorce him from all his traditional functions where hand gestures were invariably necessary, i.e., breaking bread, preaching, curing the sick, raising the dead, etc. In the Hyde portrayal one is to understand that Christ is in union with God. The noble head itself appears to be more divine than human. Rembrandt, one of the most academic of Dutch artists, gave to that divinity a universality by relating the forms of the head of Christ to the features of gods as they appear in classical art. That Rembrandt would have been accustomed to such academic idealizing can be seen in his *Aristotle Contemplating the Bust of Homer* of 1654 (Metropolitan Museum of Art, New York), where classical prototypes were very apparently joined to the models features. In the Hyde portrait the Zeus/Jupiter impression is most definite in the strong, straight nose, in the manner in which the nose joins by a curve to the brow, in the large, deep-set simplified eyes, and particularly in the detail of the roll of flesh above the left eye, a common convention in classical sculpture.

At the same time Christ remains a Jewish Jupiter. The long dark hair and beard and the high cheek bones have a distinctly Semitic cast. The original model must have been a Jew. Thus an impression of the Jesus of history is sustained in this image of Christ as the universal God.

Seymour Slive,[1] H. M. Roturmund,[2] and others have pointed out the relationship that exists between the Hyde *Portrait of Christ* and a number of small oil studies by Rembrandt of a Jewish model. Similarities to the figure of Christ as it appears in the *Christ at Emmaus* (Louvre, Paris) and in the *Hundred-Guilder Print,* as well as stylistic evidence, suggest that these studies were made in the late 1640's. The examples in the Berlin-Dahlem Museum, and in the Fogg Art Museum, Cambridge, Mass., appear to have been taken from life. It seems reasonably certain that this model was the ultimate source for the Hyde portrait. In other studies, possibly of a slightly later date, the features of the Jewish model were simplified and idealized. The two idealized examples most certainly by Rembrandt are the Christ study in the Metropolitan Museum of Art, New York, and the painting formerly in the P. de Boer Collection, Amsterdam. The idealized Christ in the John Collection, Milwaukee, is actually an enlarged version of the Metropolitan Museum study. Out-of-sight, and therefore to be questioned as to authenticity, is the head once in the H.

Weyers Collection, Tilburgh. Two other studies, one in the Bredius Museum, The Hague, and the other in The Detroit Institute of Art, seem to be of a different model with a more rounded head, while the Christ study in the Johnson Collection, Philadelphia Museum of Art, seems to be a compromise between the appearance of the two models.

The evidence is certain that Rembrandt was involved with the Christ-type of the Hyde portrait in the late 1640's and early 1650's. Therefore the late date of 1660-61 given to this work by most scholars must be questioned. (H. M. Roturmund doubts this late date on similar grounds,[3] while Otto Benesch places the work close to 1650,[4] which seems too early.) A date c. 1656 is preferable, for this work would naturally fall at the culmination of a series of artistic projects involving the figure of Christ. The Hyde painting was neither signed nor dated by Rembrandt, thus the date given must be based on stylistic grounds. However, before 1976, when a great deal of overpaint was removed, the actual style must have been partly obscured. Throughout the face were touches of later paint. The sleeves and the left hand were entirely reworked. After conservation, the smooth, faintly glistening face that has emerged resembles Rembrandt's style of 1655-57. Laboratory studies of the Hyde *Portrait of Christ* suggest the possibility that the painting might have been executed in two campaigns some years apart. Paint losses revealed what appeared to be earlier finished work by Rembrandt of a somewhat different coloristic tone. X-rays also showed that, in its earlier form, the arms of Christ were not crossed; a left hand was revealed in a lower position and down to the right.

Since the Hyde *Portrait of Christ* is definitely derived from the small oil studies of the late 1640's, the question must be raised as to whether these studies would have remained in Rembrandt's studio as late as 1660. The inventory of the artist's possessions made in 1656 lists three portraits of Christ, but they may well have been dispersed in the sale of his effects in 1657. That this was the case is suggested by the fact that a very different model appears in two definitely late portraits of Christ, the one in the Bache Collection (Metropolitan Museum of Art, New York) which is signed and dated 1661, and the other in the *Risen Christ* (Pinakothek, Munich).

W. R. Valentiner originally advanced a theory repeated by Rosenberg, Goldscheider, and Slive, that the Hyde *Portrait of Christ* was to be one of a group of eighteen portraits projected by Rembrandt in 1661, to include Mary, Jesus, the Four Evangelists, the Apostles, and other saints, possibly Paul and Barnabas.[5] But the format of the paintings associated with this project is not precisely that of the Hyde portrait, the figures being larger in relationship to the canvas, and closer to the plane of the picture. In fact the Hyde portrait is more similar in arrangement to a series of half-length apostles of 1657, which includes the *St. Paul* (National Gallery of Art, Washington, D.C.), and the *St. Bartholomew* (Timken Art Gallery, San Diego).

Against the background of Dutch seventeenth century art, with its small, naturalistic renderings of the Dutch scene, the scale and subject matter of Rembrandt's art appear both peculiar and radical. Large scale portraits of holy persons come from the Byzantine-Italian tradition. The Hyde *Portrait of Christ* appears more like an icon than do even the images in Venetian and Baroque Italian art from where such half-length portraits of saints were probably derived. It is only in the icon that we find Jesus so utterly divorced from activity. The isolation of the figure is also an instance of Rembrandt's classicizing the form, giving it the heroic isolation of an antique sculpture. At the same time it makes the work a true portrait and not, as in the case with most Christ images, a segment of a transpiring event.

Rembrandt's choice of subjects may be explained by the fact that his first training in Leyden was from artists who specialized in history painting: first, Jacob van Swanenburgh, who had spent many years in Italy; then, Pieter Lastman, the leading history painter in Holland. Horst Gerson observes that this was actually a conservative tradition with its roots in sixteenth century art. Rembrandt quite consciously sought what could be considered a universal greatness in art, identifying himself with the Italian masters from Leonardo da Vinci and Raphael to Caravaggio. In the art of his own time he could find that tradition powerfully perpetuated in the paintings of the Flemish master, Peter Paul Rubens. Thus, more than any other Dutch artist, Rembrandt may be associated with the international Baroque that had its roots in Italy. His clients would be from the Dutch intellectual community and from abroad. His art was certainly known in Italy since one of his principal patrons was a Sicilian, Antonio Ruffo. Significantly, the Hyde *Portrait of Christ* first turned up in Rome, in the sale of the art collection of Cardinal Joseph Fesch.

According to Hofstede de Groot the painting was etched by Schmidt, Barnet, and A. L. Gilbert. A photograph made in 1874 by Braun and Company was seen by Valentiner in the Berlin Print Room. Described as poor, this is probably the source of the misleading illustration that appeared in *Klassiker der Kunst* and in Bredius.

1. Seymour Slive, "An Unpublished Head of Christ by Rembrandt," *The Art Bulletin,* XLVII, December 1965, pp. 406-417.
2. H. M. Roturmund, "Wandlungen des Christus-Tiypus bei Rembrandt," *Wallraf-Richartz Jahrbuch,* XVIII, 1956, pp. 233-234, illustrated.
3. *Ibid.*
4. Otto Benesch, "Worldly and Religious Portraits in Rembrandt's Late Art," *The Art Quarterly,* XIX, Winter 1956, p. 348, illustrated p. 350.
5. W. R. Valentiner, "The Rembrandt Exhibition in Holland, 1956," *The Art Quarterly,* XIX, Winter 1956, p. 400.

Provenance: Cardinal Joseph Fesch (Napoleon's minister in Rome) 1845; DeForcade, Paris, 1873; Charles Sedelmeyer, Paris; Bamberger, Paris; Count Alexander Orloff Davidoff, Petrograd; purchased from the Soviet Union, 1933.

Literature: Wilhelm Bode, *Studiender Geschichte der Hollandischen Malerei,* Brunswick, 1883, p. 522, catalogue p. 603, no. 352; Eugène Dutuit, *Tableaux et Dessins de Rembrandt,* Paris, 1885, p. 54; Emil Michel, *Rembrandt, Sa Vie, Son Oeuvre, et Son Temps,* Paris, 1893, pp. 443 and 567, illustrated p. 445; Emil Michel, London ed., 1895, II, p. 125, illustrated p. 127; Wilhelm Bode and Cornelius Hofstede de Groot, *The Complete Work of Rembrandt,* Paris, 1901, VI, no. 415; Wilhelm R. Valentiner, *Rembrandt, der Meisters Gemälde (Klassiker der Kunst),* Stuttgart and Berlin, 1907, no. 392, illustrated; French ed., no date, same no. as preceding; Cornelius Hofstede de Groot, *A Catalogue Raisonné of the Works of the Most Eminent Dutch Painters of the Seventeenth Century,* London, VI, 1916, p. 118, no. 162; Werner Weisbach, *Rembrandt,* Berlin and Leipzig, 1926, p. 498, fig. 150; Abraham Bredius, *The Paintings of Rembrandt,* Vienna, 1936, no. 628, illustrated; German ed., Vienna, 1935; George Henry McCall and William R. Valentiner, *Catalogue of European Paintings and Sculpture from 1300-1800, Masterpieces of Art, New York World's Fair,* May to October, 1939, New York, 1939, p. 150, no. 308, pl. 69; Duveen Galleries, New York, *Paintings by the Great Dutch Masters of the Seventeenth Century,* October 8-November 7, 1942, New York, 1942, catalogue by George Henry McCall and Adriaan J. Barnouw, p. 69, no. 49, illustrated p. 141; The Art Association of Montreal, *Five Centuries of Dutch Art,* March 9-April 19, 1944, Montreal,

1944, p. 32, no. 44, illustrated p. 72; The Fogg Art Museum, Harvard, *Rembrandt; Paintings and Etchings,* Cambridge, Mass., October 19-November 27, 1948, no. 10; Otto Benesch, *op. cit.;* H. M. Roturmund, *op. cit.;* W. R. Valentiner, *op. cit.;* Ludwig Goldscheider, *Rembrandt, Paintings, Drawings, and Etchings,* London, 1960, p. 182, no. 111, illustrated; F. Lane Faison, Jr., *Art Tours and Detours in New York State,* New York, 1964, p. 114, fig. 190; Seymour Slive, *op. cit.,* p. 415, fig. 13; Kurt Bauch, *Rembrandt Gemälde,* Berlin, 1966, no. 229; Horst Gerson, *Rembrandt Paintings,* Amsterdam, 1968, pp. 428, 502, fig. 368; James K. Kettlewell, *Rembrandt's Christ in Thirteen Paintings and One Etching,* The Hyde Collection, Glens Falls, N.Y., 1968, illustrated, pp. 4 and 6; Horst Gerson, *The Complete Edition of the Paintings of A. Bredius,* revised ed., London, 1969, p. 614, no. 628, illustrated p. 529.

Exhibitions: The Austrian Museum, Vienna, 1873; Palais du Corps Legislatif, Paris, 1874; Museum of Fine Arts, Moscow, c. 1930; Masterpieces of Art Exhibition, New York World's Fair, 1939; Duveen Galleries, New York, for the benefit of the Women's Voluntary Services and Queen Wilhelmina Fund, 1942; The Art Association of Montreal, 1944; The Fogg Art Museum, Cambridge, Mass., 1948.

52. Jacob van Ruisdael

Dutch, 1629-1682

Landscape Near Castle Bentheim, c. 1653

Oil on wooden panel. 28.5 x 28.2 cm. (11-5/8 x 11-1/8″) 1971.42
Signed in monogram lower center: "JR."

The approximate date and location of this painting may be recognized because of the close similarity of the landscape to the foreground section of Ruisdael's *Landscape with Castle Bentheim* (Gemaeldegalerie, Dresden).[1] The grouping of trees, the road, even the figures are unmistakably taken from the same position. In the Dresden painting the castle is on a high slope at the right. A corner of it appears where a fragment of cloud occurs in the Hyde painting.

Ruisdael was born in the Netherlands, in Haarlem. He studied painting with his uncle Salomon van Ruisdael, and in 1648 he was accepted into the Haarlem painters' guild. From 1650 to 1657 he traveled extensively, and then settled in Amsterdam. During some of these years of travel and study Ruisdael must have visited Bentheim in Germany, for he painted approximately fourteen views in which the castle, still extant, can be identified. Two of these are dated—the first in 1651, the second in 1653. The indication is that Ruisdael was here for some time, perhaps three or four years.

In the paintings executed during his travels, Ruisdael developed an inclination for powerful and romantic effects quite different from the straight-forward landscape views of the tradition of Jan van Goyen, Salomon van Ruisdael and Pieter Molijn, in which he had been trained. While Hercules Seghers and Rembrandt had already romanticized nature in their landscapes, their views were more distant and grandiose than Ruisdael's. In this period of his career Ruisdael dramatized the close views of the Molijn tradition (see number 47 in this catalogue). As in the Hyde work, a great dark tree usually dominates the scene, while part of the view invariably extends to a far horizon.

The style of the foreground and tree are distinctly Ruisdael's, rich with detail and translucent shadows. The sky is curiously heavy in treatment, and there is evidence of later reworking.

1. Jakob Rosenberg, *Jacob van Ruisdael,* Berlin, 1928, no. 13.

Provenance: Purchased from Zacharie Birtschansky, Paris, 1938.

53. Style of Jan Vermeer

possibly Han van Meegeren

Dutch, 1889-1947

Girl with Blue Bow, c. 1925

Aqueous medium over old oil paint on old canvas. 33 x 25 cm. (13 x 9-7/8″) 1971.56

This is a simple portrait of a young girl, her body posed without any sign of motion, at a slight angle to the picture surface. The eyes look directly out, the face is without distinct expression, the mouth closed and at rest. It is these larger aspects of the work that resemble least the style of the Dutch seventeenth century painter Jan Vermeer. Vermeer's figures are invariably involved in some actual or potential motion, the most famous instance being the *Head of a Girl with Pearl Ear Drops* (Mauritshuis, The Hague, Holland). Furthermore, the faces of Vermeer's typical figures always have distinct, though often subtle expressions. Usually the lips are parted, which is a dramatic device to impart a sense of breathing life and fleeting thought to a portrait image. In a more general sense these are characteristic of the seventeenth century Baroque style. By contrast, the figure in the Hyde portrait is without dramatic tension of any sort. The *Girl with Blue Bow* looks stolidly ahead, a mere object with only the superficial trappings of Vermeer's style. Even the colors, which would seem to be Vermeer's, lack the extraordinary translucency characteristic of the colors in an authentic work.

The *Girl with Blue Bow* first appeared on the scene in March 1934 at a sale at the London auction house of Christie's. It was listed as being from the collection of a Charles E. Carruthers, Batheaston, Somerset, England and sold for the low price of £504. Years later, when the authenticity of the work was being seriously questioned, Charles Carruthers wrote to the dealer Hanns Schaeffer (who had sold the picture to Mrs. Hyde), that "the painting had been hanging in my father's house in 1933 and 1934."[1] During an investigation conducted by Joseph Dodge, father of the then Curator of The Hyde Collection, Carruthers claimed the painting has been in the possession of his family "for several generations."[2]

The noted art historian, Tancred Borenius, in an article in the *Burlington Magazine,* June 1935, enthusiastically supported the authenticity of the work.[3] In July 1935 it was exhibited at the Boymans Museum, Rotterdam. From that point Vermeer scholars either supported or opposed the painting's authenticity.[4] Doubts became so strong that, when the painting was to be exhibited in Montreal in 1944, it was Mrs. Hyde's suggestion that it be designated as "attributed to" Vermeer.[5]

In its vicissitudes the painting was restored by William Suhr in 1937. Most early references to it indicate that it was badly in need of restoration, as it is today, due to the peculiar reaction of the aqueous medium with the atmosphere.

In 1958 the *Girl with Blue Bow* was submitted to laboratory analysis at the Museum of Fine Arts, Boston, by conservators William Young and Morton Bradley. The conclusion was reached that the work was definitely a forgery. X-rays indicated that the old canvas support, which showed a different crackle pattern, had been cut from another work. Chemical analysis proved the paint medium not to be oil. The intention of the forger was to simulate the ability of ancient oil paint to resist solvents. Bradley speculated that the medium was the modern synthetic material, phenolformaldehyde, first used by the famous Vermeer forger, Han van Meegeren. Paul Coremans, the expert on van Meegeren's faked Vermeers, saw the Hyde painting while it was at the Museum of Fine Arts. As noted in a letter from William Young, "he was in agreement with our findings that the painting was an imitation of Vermeer and had some characteristics of an early van Meegeren forgery."[6] Thus the evidence is indicative, but not at all firm, that van Meegeren painted the *Girl with Blue Bow.*

In 1964 the painting was subjected to an even more rigorous laboratory analysis, using larger samples for testing. Sheldon Keck at the Conservation Center of the Institute of Fine Arts, New York University, in New York City conducted these tests. Two significant determinations were made: first, that the medium in all paint layers was aqueous with a protein base, a description which would fit such traditional painting media as egg yolk, casein, gum arabic, or glue. Apparently this would rule out the possibility of the synthetic medium phenolformaldehyde and make less certain the attribution to van Meegeren. Vermeer himself never used an aqueous medium, though this would not be sufficiently firm ground upon which to reject the authenticity of the work.

The second important determination made by Sheldon Keck and corroborated by others, would indicate more certainly that the work was a forgery: that the blue pigment in the blue bow proved to be a modern ultramarine, and not the early ultramarine blue of Vermeer, which was made from ground lapis lazuli. This conclusion was independently confirmed by R. J. Gettens, Richard D. Buck, and again by Paul Coremans, all noted specialists in the laboratory analysis of art.

The evidence would, in fact, indicate that the Hyde's Vermeer is a forgery. Paul Coremans noted the similarity in paint structure in two paintings attributed to Vermeer which he analyzed in the National Gallery of Art, Washington, D.C., *The Smiling Girl* and *The Lacemaker.*[7] The indication is that these two paintings are forgeries by the same hand.

1. Photostat of original letter from Schaeffer with Carruther's quote in Hyde Archives.
2. Letter from A. W. Mellows of The Bankers Trust Company, London to Joseph Dodge quoting the manager of their Midland Bank Ltd. branch, who had called on Mr. Carruthers in May, 1959.
3. Tancred Borenius, "Old Masters at the Ver Meer Gallery," *Burlington Magazine,* LXVI, June, 1935, p. 298, illustrated, p. XXIII.
4. In favor of: T. Borenius; W. R. Valentiner (certificate dated July 1, 1935), F. M. Davis, G. Isarlov, P. L. Hale; against: P. T. A. Swillens (1940 ed.), A. B. DeVries (1948 ed.), L. Goldscheider, G. Ungaretti and P. Beanconi. See Literature below.
5. Letter from C. F. Martin, April 1944, in which Mrs. Hyde was informed that her suggestion was not to be followed.
6. Letter from William Young, February 17, 1959.
7. Copy of letter to Sheldon Keck, December 13, 1963. Coremans does not indicate which two paintings he is referring to, but the similarities of the Hyde work to *The Smiling Girl* and *The Lacemaker* are sufficiently evident. Arthur Wheelock, Jr., Curator of Dutch and Flemish Painting at the National Gallery of Art, Washington, in a manuscript to be published, shows that these two paintings are in the same peculiar medium as the Hyde work. He believes they are by Theo van Wijngaarden, a teacher of van Meegeren.

Provenance: Charles E. Carruthers, Batheaston, Somerset, England; A. F. Reyre, London; D. Katz, Dieren, Netherlands; Hanns Schaeffer, New York; purchased from Schaeffer Galleries, Inc., New York, April 1937.

Literature: Christie, Manson and Woods, London, March 23, 1934, no. 62; Tancred Borenius, *op. cit.;* Frank M. Davis, "An auctioned ugly duckling becomes a swan: a Vermeer revealed," *Illustrated London News,* April 20, 1935, pp. 660-661, figs. 1, 2; Museum Boymans, Rotterdam, *Vermeer Vorsprong en invloed Fabritius, De Hooch, DeWitte,* July 9-October 9, 1935, p. 38, no. 88; George Isarlov, "Vermeer à l'exposition de Rotterdam," *La Renaissance de l'art,* XVIII, no. 10, 1935, p. 102; Philip L. Hale, *Vermeer,* Boston and New York, 1937, p. 162, pl. 37; P. T. A. Swillens, *Johannes Vermeer, Painter of Delft, 1632-1675,* Utrecht and Brussels, 1940, p. 65, no. H; Thomas Bodkin, *The Paintings of Jan Vermeer,* New York, 1940, pp. 5-6, illustrated p. 6; The Art Association of Montreal, *Five Centuries of Dutch Art,* Montreal, March 9-April 9, 1944, p. 44, no. 79, illustrated p. 86; Ary Bob DeVries, *Jan Vermeer of Delft,* London and New York, Toronto and Sidney, 1948, p. 97, pl. 36 (revised from the 1939 and 1945 eds.), no. 20, p. 85, 1939 ed.; Ludwig Goldscheider, *Jan Vermeer,* London and New York, 1958, no. VII, illustrated; Giuseppi Ungaretti and Piero Beanconi, *L'Opera Completa di Vermeer,* Milan, 1967, p. 90, no. 17, illustrated p. 91, London ed. 1970.

Exhibitions: Boymans Museum, Rotterdam, July 9-October 9, 1935; Art Association of Montreal, *Five Centuries of Dutch Art,* March 9-April 9, 1944.

54. Edwaert Colyer

Dutch, active 1673-1702

Vanitas Still Life, c. 1684

Oil on canvas. 35.8 x 30.2 cm. (14-1/8 x 11-7/8″) 1971.12

The authorship and suggested date for this work are assured by the fact that there exists in the David Hultmark Collection, Saltsjöbaden, Sweden, a still life that almost exactly duplicates the Hyde painting except for the addition, behind the still life objects, of a self-portrait of the artist holding a drawing of a woman. The painting is signed and dated 1684.[1]

While Colyer was an artist of modest quality, the work is a study rich in meaning and associations. He specialized in what was known, even in the seventeenth century, as the Vanitas still life subjects. The Vanitas still life was developed in the city of Leyden, in the ambience of the university, where there was great interest in artistic symbolism at that time. The university itself was a center of Calvinist moralizing, and the point made by the Vanitas still life is that man's pride in his attainments is pure vanity; that all his achievements are meaningless in the face of death. Even the favorite old saying "VITA BREVIS, ARS LONGA" (life is short, art long) is presented here as a vanity. Not obvious on the far right of the painting is a slip of paper in a book with the words "MEMENTO MORI" (remember death).

The books and globe refer to the contemplative life; the wine glass and tobacco were a stock symbol of gratification of the senses. Curiously, the musical instruments, which may depict a branch of the arts, also represent the sin of lust. This interpretation is given emphasis by the presence on the table of the grinning goat-like face of a faun in what appears to be a feathered cap. The faun is one of the more familiar symbols of lust. The faun mask is absent from the self-portrait in Sweden, but the portrait of a woman held by the artist may make the same point in a more gentle fashion. Thus the artist groups together both the higher and lower pursuits of mankind as being equally vain. The anti-humanist nature of such a point of view is a purely Calvinist sentiment.

---

1. Information on Colyer and the Vanitas still life was derived from Ingvar Bergström, *Dutch Still-Life Painting in the Seventeenth Century,* New York ed., 1956, p. 154 ff.

55. School of Frans van Mieris the Elder

Dutch

The Oyster Meal, c. 1700

Oil on copper. 27.8 x 20.85 cm. (10-15/16 x 8-3/16″) 1971.53

Otto Naumann has identified twenty-nine replicas of the painting by Frans van Mieris entitled *The Oyster Meal* (Mauritshuis Museum, The Hague, Holland).[1] Naumann considers this to be one of the best of the replicas, and possibly the work of Willem van Mieris, the artist's son. In a catalogue in preparation of van Mieris' work, Naumann dates the Hyde painting early in the eighteenth century. That the painting is a replica is indicated by the fact that the artist has omitted certain details visible in the Mauritshuis version, such as a ring on the man's finger. Naumann also observes that the man's facial expression is different, the smile being more obvious.

Frans van Mieris was born in Delft in 1635 and died in Leyden in 1681. In his own time, and in the eighteenth and nineteenth centuries, he was a celebrated painter. His art was immensely popular, which accounts for the unusual number of replicas of this subject and of other paintings by him.

The Oyster Meal in the Mauritshuis is signed and dated 1661. Like the similar subject matter of Gerard Ter Borch, it is representative of the aristocratic genre themes which were popular at the time. As did Ter Borch, the artist made a *tour de force* of his rendering of shiny surfaces—metal, satin, etc. Genre subjects of this sort with a muted erotic theme (the oysters are considered to be an aphrodisiac) were common in Dutch art of the period. The artist presents the viewer with a carefully staged drama, which is intended to be amusing. The arched format is curious, since it was the familiar way of framing sacred themes in Catholic art. Van Mieris would have learned this format from his teacher, Rembrandt's famous pupil Gerard Dou.

---

1. From a manuscript to be published as part of a catalogue raisonné by Otto Naumann. Naumann points out that Horst Gerson and E. H. Havercamp-Begemann also considered the Hyde painting to be a copy.

Provenance: Purchased from Herman Ball, Berlin, 1925. Naumann (see note above) cites a replica on copper, the same size as the Hyde work, sold at the E. J. de Court van Valkenswaard sale, Dordrecht, April 12, 1947, no. 105, to a de la Motte, and at a "d'Eve" sale, Cologne, March 20, 1899, no. 86.

56. Claude Lorrain

French, 1600-1682

Parnassus, 1674

Pen and brown wash heightened with white on paper. 18.4 x 24.1 cm. (7-1/4 x 9-1/2″) 1971.72
Signed and dated lower right: "CLAUDIO I.V. ROMA 1674."

The view in this work is of Mt. Parnassus in a lush landscape setting, with Apollo surrounded by the nine muses on a rocky knoll. Apollo plays a violin-like instrument, showing the ultimate derivation of the composition from Raphael's famous *Parnassus* (Stanza della Segnatura, Vatican), where Apollo plays a modern *lira da braccio* rather than his traditional lyre. The poets whom Apollo and his muses inspire approach on a bridge on the lower right. In the left foreground are swans, who were creatures sacred to Apollo.

The drawing is discussed at length by Roethlisberger who describes it as "...the most monumental of the drawings in 1674..." Roethlisberger lists seven drawings from 1674 that were preparatory studies for a Parnassus subject.[1] At least four of these, including the Hyde drawing, are of the same size. This would suggest that a possible reading of the date on the Hyde drawing as 1634 would be incorrect, even though it appears more definitely as a "3" than as a "7."

Roethlisberger believes the painted composition that ultimately resulted from these drawings is the *Parnassus* of 1680[2] (Museum of Fine Arts, Boston), though the work is different, at least from the Hyde drawing, in many significant ways—i.e., the figures are grouped on the right, not the left, and there is a circular temple behind them.

The drawing is a typical Baroque landscape composition in the ideal mode, derived from late sixteenth century decorative wall paintings in Italy. This decorative landscape tradition, given a more precise balancing of tree and architectural masses by Annibale Carracci in his *Flight into Egypt* (Doria Gallery, Rome), was made vastly influential by Claude Lorrain. Engravings after Claude's ideal landscape were popular even in Colonial America and, in the nineteenth century, greatly affected the style of the English painter Turner and the American artists of the Hudson River School.

The composition of the Hyde *Parnassus* is characteristic in that the tree masses balance each other along a diagonal line which leads back into the picture, while a second diagonal path cuts into a distant space in the opposite direction. However, the Hyde composition is unusual in the degree to which the foreground is closed off by the masses of rocks and trees which allow only a narrow doorway into the distance at the right.

1. Marcel Roethlisberger, *Claude Lorrain, the Drawings,* Berkeley and Los Angeles, 1968, I, p. 394, no. 1071; II, illustrated.
2. *Ibid.*

Provenance: On the back of the drawing is a book plate of a Lord Milford of the Philipps family, who died in 1823. According to Roethlisberger the collection was formed by an E. Philipps around 1730, mainly from an old Italian collection. In 1943, the Milford Collection was sold by a London dealer named Calmann. Mrs. Hyde purchased the drawing in New York from Delius Giese, a second dealer with galleries in London and New York, December 12, 1949.

Literature: Delius Giese, *50 Drawings, Old and New,* New York Gallery, October 4-25, 1949, no. 24, illustrated; Marcel Roethlisberger, *Claude Lorrain, the Paintings,* New Haven, Conn., 1961, I, pp. 452-453; II, fig. 338a; Roethlisberger, *Claude Lorrain, the Drawings, op. cit.*

Exhibitions: Delius Giese, New York, October 4-October 25, 1949.

57. Spanish

Adoration of the Christ Child, c. 1650

Carved wood, gesso, polychrome, and gold leaf. 57.1 x 52.1 cm. (22-1/2 x 20-1/2″) 1971.84

Installed in 1912, before the completion of Hyde House, this sculpture originally would have decorated the wall of a Spanish church or convent.[1] The subject is the newborn Christ adored by figures of angels and shepherds representing heaven and earth. Unusual in such adoration subjects is the predominance of heaven's representatives, the three angels. Curiously there is only a single shepherd to stand for the earthly realm.

Further augmenting this devotional sculpture's symbolic intent is the fact that the fragments of architecture which appear represent not a humble manger but rather the glorious Church of Christ which came into existence at his advent.

Though not a masterwork, this sculpture is a perfect representation of the Baroque style of the seventeenth century. The primary characteristic of Baroque art is its emphasis on the dramatic. More often than not drama is conveyed, as here, with exaggerated motion on the part of the human figure.

The organic curves of the shell-like enframement, common in Baroque decorative art, convey a sense of motion on a more abstract level.

---

1. Considered to be Spanish when first purchased, it has never been questioned.

58. Giovanni Paolo Pannini

Italian, 1691/1692-1765

Scene in the Roman Campagna, 1725-50

Watercolor on paper over red and black chalk. 26.3 x 34.7 cm. (10-3/8 x 13-5/8″) 1971.60
Signed (?) on original mount: "Gio Paolo Panini fece."

The scene of this drawing is probably near Rome. On the left is a corner of a large villa in the Baroque style of the seventeenth or eighteenth century; on the right is a terraced garden supported by a retaining wall and surrounded with a high hedge.

Pannini arrived in Rome in 1717 and remained there until his death in 1765. He became the foremost painter of the ancient ruins of Rome, a subject very popular in the proto-romantic eighteenth century. This theme of architectural ruins in which man's mightiest works are brought down by a mightier nature, would appear to be absent from the Hyde work. It is a direct view of some specific place the artist would have visited in the *Campagna,* the countryside around Rome. An analysis of the perspective scheme in the drawing shows that the artist took his view from a position level with the top story of the building seen at the left, suggesting that Pannini drew from an upper window of another wing of the villa.

Characteristic of Pannini's style is the domestic activity of small human figures set against the largeness of architectural forms and empty space. It is also characteristic in the way architecture appears in fragments, rather than in complete views. While it is also typical of Pannini to have a deep foreground dominate the scene, one of the drawing's most attractive and unusual features is the delicate portrayal of a light-filled middle-distance of hills and open groves of trees.

59. Giambattista Tiepolo

Italian (Venetian), 1696-1770

The Madonna and Child with Saints and Bishops, c. 1732-33

Pen and wash over black chalk on white paper. 27.5 x 20.4 cm. (10-7/8 x 8-1/16") 1971.79
Inscribed on recto: "Tiepoleto D. 2" in black ink, and "N 317" in blue ink.

Standard for Baroque altarpieces, this subject of an enthroned Virgin Mary with saints was repeated many times in Tiepolo's art. However, the particular arrangement here cannot be recognized among Tiepolo's extant works. A martyred bishop saint is being received by the Queen of Heaven in her heavenly throne room. Mary is seated on a solid podium, not on the bank of clouds that is used by artists to suggest that she has descended to a lower sphere. The genuflecting central figure carries a bishop's crozier, while what appears to be a mitre lies beside him on the ground. On the left an angel bearing a martyr's palm branch refers to the bishop's martyrdom. On the right, faintly seen in shadow, John the Baptist can be identified by his attribute, the small cross. The fact that a coat-of-arms is sketched on the bishop's back perhaps indicates that this martyred bishop was of a family recognizable in the church where the final alterpiece was to be placed. This may be, as George Knox suggests, the martyred St. John, Bishop of Bergamo.[1] Ten years later, in 1743, Tiepolo was to paint a *Martyrdom of St. John of Bergamo.* Behind the enthroned Virgin two *putti* hold a cloth of honor, a motif that appears in the oil sketch of another Tiepolo enthroned Madonna in the Hyde (number 60) and in a number of his other works.

The drawing was begun with an extremely quick sketch in black chalk. To this was applied the more visible drawing of quick-moving pen strokes and ink washes. With such drawings Tiepolo developed his first concepts for compositions. In his technique the artist reduced the physical world to no more than a dramatic play of lights and shades. Lines never do more than suggest shapes within the flickering darks and lights. The point is to achieve an evocative artistic motion. In the drawings of Poussin, Rembrandt, and other Baroque artists, one often finds a similar restriction of the drawing media to the rendering of shadow, though of all Baroque artists, Tiepolo may be the least restrained in his bypassing of objective reality for expressive effects.

1. George Knox, Fogg Art Museum, *Tiepolo: A Bicentenary Exhibition, 1770-1970,* Cambridge, Mass., 1970, no. 12, illustrated.

Provenance: Bellingham-Smith sale, Amsterdam, July 5, 1927, lot 128; purchased first by Dan Fellows Platt, then Kleinberger (dealer ?); sold from unidentified private collection at Parke-Bernet Galleries, Inc., New York, January 23, 1947; purchased from the Schaeffer Galleries, Inc., New York, 1947.

Literature: Detlev von Hadeln, *Handzeichnungen von G. B. Tiepolo,* Munich, 1927, pl. 98, English ed., N.Y., 1970, p. 22, pl. 98; *Schaeffer Galleries Bulletin,* March 1, 1947, no. 52; George Knox, *op. cit.*

Exhibitions: Fogg Art Museum, March 14-May 3, 1970, *Tiepolo: A Bicentenary Exhibition, 1770-1970.*

60. Giambattista Tiepolo

Italian (Venetian), 1696-1770

Madonna and Child with St. Catherine and the Infant St. John, c. 1755-60

Oil on canvas. 47.6 x 27.6 cm. (18-3/4 x 10-7/8") 1971.47

Most of Tiepolo's work was designed for specific architectural settings; either for ceilings, which he would cover with commemorative allegorical themes, or for altarpieces which eulogized the Virgin Mary, Christ, and the Saints of the Roman Catholic Church. The Hyde *Madonna and Child with St. Catherine and the Infant St. John* is an oil sketch for a typical Baroque altarpiece. Presumably it was prepared as a model for presentation to the artist's patrons. Since a full-scale altarpiece of this subject by Tiepolo cannot be found, it may be that this composition was rejected and replaced by an alternative.

The design of the composition is characteristically late Baroque in the way the figures of the infant St. John, St. Catherine of Alexandria, and the Virgin Mary are organized along an **S** curve. Mary holds the Christ Child who is shown partly standing on her lap and looking down at St. John. Behind Mary a cloth of honor is suspended by angels. St. John can be identified by his staff which lies beside him on the ground, by his camel's hair robe, and by the lamb he carries. St. Catherine's identifying attribute, the broken wheel, is to the right of the column. She carries a martyr's palm branch, symbol of her ultimate victory. (Morassi, who apparently did not see the wheel, identified this figure as St. Giustina.[1]) St. Catherine leans on the broken column, a common symbol of the Virgin Mary. In the background is a fragment of a Roman triumphal arch. Appearing often in Tiepolo's art, this triumphal arch may refer to the triumph over death that is possible through the Church and its saints.

The inclusion of Sts. Catherine and John together occurs on only one other occasion in Tiepolo's art, in his reworking of a *Mystic Marriage of St. Catherine* (Hausammann Collection, Zürich), from the workshop of the earlier Venetian painter Paolo Veronese.[2] In the Veronese version, however, St. John is mature. The presence of John in the Hyde work may be a reference to the importance of baptism in one of the many St. Catherine legends. The Virgin Mary appeared to her in a dream holding the Christ Child. The Virgin asked Jesus to accept Catherine as his servant, but he refused for the curious reason that she was insufficiently beautiful. Upon awakening and seeking a way to please the Christ Child, Catherine had herself baptized. This ultimately led to her becoming the mystical bride of Christ. St. John's presence in both the Hyde painting and the re-worked Veronese may be a reference to this baptism.

Though this compositional arrangement with the Virgin Mary and Christ on clouds above, and with saints below on the earth, was standard for such subjects in the Baroque period, the work is distinctively Late Baroque in style because of the **S** curve of its composition, its fresh, bright tonality, and its shallow, almost flat spacial effect.

1. Antonio Morassi, *A Complete Catalogue of the Paintings of G. B. Tiepolo,* Greenwich, Conn., 1962, p. 35, fig. 101.
2. *Ibid.,* p. 69, fig. 108.

Provenance: Purchased from Lilienfeld Galleries, New York, in 1941. It is possible that the original owner was a David Sellar, since on the stretcher is the curious inscription "Martin H. Colnaghi from his friend David Sellar, in memory of happy days at 11 Haymarket 1886." It is not clear whether there were intermediate owners between Colnaghi and Lilienfeld.

Literature: Antonio Morassi, *op. cit.;* S. Lane Faison, Jr., *Art Tours and Detours in New York State,* New York, 1964, p. 115, fig. 192; Birmingham Museum of Art, *The Tiepolos: Painters to Princes and Prelates,* Birmingham, Ala., 1978, no. 21, p. 79, illustrated, pp. 12 and 136.

Exhibitions: Royal Academy, *Exhibit of Works by Old Masters,* London, 1888; Birmingham Museum of Art, Birmingham, Ala., January 8-February 19, 1978; Museum of Fine Arts, Springfield, March 19-May 7, 1978.

61. Giambattista Tiepolo

Italian (Venetian), 1696-1770

The Christ Child, c. 1767-69

Red and white chalk on a blue-green paper; watermark: "MW." 20.3 x 29 cm. (8 x 11-3/8″) 1971.80
On verso: "CM" (crossed out with three horizontal lines)"No. 3316" (ink); "699" (pencil).

This drawing can be identified with certainty as a study for an important altarpiece of St. Joseph and the Christ Child, painted by Tiepolo late in his career for the chapel of the Royal Palace at Aranjuez, near Madrid, between 1767 and 1769. At some subsequent date the altarpiece was broken up, but a large fragment still survives in The Detroit Art Institute. In this surviving fragment Joseph appears holding the infant Jesus in his arms, a rare image in art. The fact that the Child smiles in the Hyde version, but appears more serious in the Detroit rendering, indicates that the drawing precedes the painting and is a preparatory study for it.[1]

The medium, red and white chalk on blue-green paper, was a favorite of Venetian painters from early in the sixteenth century. This type of drawing would have been taken from the living model, as one step in a process which, in Tiepolo's case, would have begun with free compositional studies in pen and ink wash, like The Hyde Collection's *Madonna and Child with Saints and Bishops* (number 59). When a satisfactory composition was arrived at, detailed studies of the model such as this would have been made. Tiepolo's final step would have been a small oil sketch similar to The Hyde Collection's *Madonna with St. Catherine and the Infant St. John* (number 60).

A peculiar characteristic of Venetian draftsmanship in the eighteenth century was the nervous, vibrating line, so evident here in the outline surrounding the infant's form. It is as if the motion that appeared in the large design of earlier Baroque art were now reduced to a delicate agitation of outlines.

1. George Knox, Fogg Art Museum, *Tiepolo: A Bicentenary Exhibition, 1770-1970,* Cambridge, Mass., 1970, no. 97, illustrated.

Provenance: There are no documents pertaining to this work in the Hyde Archives. In the Fogg exhibition catalogue, the names of two previous owners are given: Bossi and Beyerlen. This is a reference to one of the two great sources of Tiepolo drawings in modern collections, the Bossi-Beyerlen Sale held in Stuttgart on March 27, 1882, when some 850 Tiepolo drawings were sold. Up to that time they had remained in the albums in which Tiepolo himself had mounted them.

Literature: George Knox, *op. cit.;* Birmingham Museum of Art, *The Tiepolos: Painters to Princes and Prelates,* Birmingham, Ala., 1978, p. 95, no. 73, illustrated, p. 97.

Exhibitions: Fogg Art Museum, Cambridge, Mass., March 14-May 3, 1970; Birmingham Museum of Art, Birmingham, Ala., January 8-February 19, 1978; Museum of Fine Arts, Springfield, March 19-May 7, 1978.

62. Francesco Zuccarelli

Italian, 1702-1788

Italian Landscape, c. 1755-75

Black and sepia ink over red chalk on paper. 27 x 42.4 cm. (11 x 17-1/2″) 1971.82

Typical of Zuccarelli's landscape compositions, the scene is more than likely purely imaginative. Derived from the scenery of the *Campagna,* the countryside around Rome, the view is of a tamed landscape with peasants in the foreground and a picturesque town in the middle-distance. The ultimate reference for such scenes is the idealization of rural life in the lengthy poem, *The Georgics* by the Roman poet Virgil.

The art of landscape painting as a form of wall decoration originated in Roman times and was revived in sixteenth century Venice. In the seventeenth century such artists as Annibale Carracci and Claude Lorrain had popularized it in easel painting. In the eighteenth century landscape became the preferred theme for the decoration of interiors in easel and wall paintings. Thus the function performed by most of Zuccarelli's work would have been a decorative one.

In the early eighteenth century the Venetian painter Marco Ricci had gone to England where he popularized the Italian landscape. Zuccarelli was trained in Rome but later travelled to Venice where he must have been greatly influenced by Ricci's style. Later, when Zuccarelli went to England, he capitalized on the popularity of Italian landscape subjects. Until 1782 he was in London where he was a founder of the Royal Academy in 1768. The majority of his paintings remain in English collections.

63. Francesco or Giacomo Guardi ?

Italian (Venetian)

Venice, the Arsenal, late eighteenth century

Oil on canvas. 48.9 x 68.5 cm. (19-1/8 x 27") 1971.20

The view is taken from the Fondamenta d'Arsenale in Venice. On the left appears the main entrance to the Arsenal, and in the distance is the tower of the Church of San Francesco della Vigna. The Arsenal lies on a point of land due east of the Piazza San Marco.

Although entirely in the manner of Francesco Guardi, the great Venetian *veduta* painter, Francesco's authorship of this work must be questioned. In spite of endorsements by Daniel Catton Rich, W. R. Valentiner, and John Constable, the style of the Hyde work appears to be less sharp than Guardi's and has less contrast of light and shadow.

The Hyde painting is very close in arrangement to two views of the Venice Arsenal by Francesco Guardi himself; one (Morassi 608), Museum of Fine Arts, Boston; the other (Morassi 607), Kunsthistorisches Museum, Vienna.[1] Close also to the Hyde painting is a drawing in the Janos Scholz Collection, New York, which is signed by Francesco's son Giacomo Guardi. It is tempting to consider this painting as Giacomo's. Whatever its authorship, the Hyde painting certainly originated in the Guardi circle and is an excellent example of its time and place in art history. The style is Late Baroque.

Guardi's views interpret rather than describe Venice. With a loose brush he orchestrated humanity, architecture, boats, and sky into a unified scheme where the parts are drastically subordinated to the whole. This manner of painting originated in the more purely decorative landscapes of Guardi's Venetian predecessor, Marco Ricci. Ricci's style, in turn, is derived from a form of romantic landscape developed in the late Renaissance in Italy specifically for wall decoration and has its counterpart in a style of wall decoration found in ancient Rome.

1. The Hyde painting does not appear in Antonio Morassi's *Guardi,* Venice, 1973, though Morassi describes other Guardi's of the same subject. (Numbers 607, 608 and three other views of the Arsenal of a somewhat different format.)

Provenance: Lilienfeld Galleries, New York; purchased from Mortimer J. Brandt, New York, 1950. It was reputed to be from the collection of an English nobleman.

64. François Boucher

French, 1703-1770

Vertumnus and Pomona, c. 1763

Black chalk heightened with white on buff paper. Oval field. 29 x 25.6 cm. (11-7/16 x 10-1/16″) 1971.61
Blind stamp lower center and lower right: "GLOMY," Lugt 119.

The legend of the two ancient deities, Vertumnus and Pomona, one of the many tales from the Latin poet Ovid's *Metamorphoses,* is recounted by Boucher in drawings, paintings, and in designs for tapestries.[1] Vertumnus, who was the god of orchards and patron god of bartering, had the ability to change his appearance at will. In unsuccessful attempts to woo the wise and chaste nymph Pomona, goddess of orchards and gardens, he had transformed himself into a woodsman, a soldier, and vineyard worker. He was finally able to tell her of his love and win her affection by approaching her in the disguise of an old woman;[2] the subject of the Hyde drawing.

The drawing appears to be a preparatory study for an extremely similar painting by Boucher in the Louvre, Paris, and dated 1763. The one important difference in the painting is that Pomona holds a flower to her face, whereas in the Hyde version, both arms are lowered. In 1757 Boucher painted a somewhat similar *Vertumnus and Pomona* (Palace of the Legion of Honor, San Francisco). In this painting the figures are similarly posed, though in the background a statue of a woman replaces the ornamental urn and Pomona holds two flowers to her face.[3]

The composition of the Louvre painting also appears in a series of Gobelin tapestries ordered in 1763 by George Williams, Earl of Coventry, for his country house Croome Court in Worcestershire, England.[4] It was at the time when Boucher was Director of the Gobelin factory. The tapestries were installed in a room designed for them by the great architect Robert Adam. The room along with its tapestries is now in the Metropolitan Museum of Art, New York, and was a gift of the Samuel Kress Foundation in 1958.

In these tapestries four oval medallions appear surrounded by a red field. The four mythological subjects are allegories representing the four essential elements; air, earth, fire, and water, with the Vertumnus and Pomona subject representing earth.

Boucher may have been directed to his interest in the study of Vertumnus and Pomona by his famous patroness Madame de Pompadour, mistress of King Louis XV. In 1749, in a play written and directed by herself and entitled *La Terre* (Earth), she played the part of Pomona, following essentially Ovid's tale.[5]

1. Research by Jane Rehl.
2. *Metamorphoses of Ovid,* trans. A. E. Watts, Los Angeles, 1954, p. 338.
3. Thomas C. Howe, *Bulletin, Palace of the Legion of Honor,* San Francisco, New Series, I, March and April, 1968.
4. Edith A. Standen, "Croome Court: the Tapestries," *The Metropolitan Museum of Art Bulletin,* November 1959, pp. 96-112.
5. Emile Compardon, *Mme. de Pompadour et la Cour de Louis XV au milieu du dix-huitième siècle,* Paris, 1867, pp. 112 and 372.

Literature: Howe, *op. cit.,* fig. 7; A. Ananoff, *L'Oeuvre dessiné de François Boucher,* II, Paris, 1966, pp. 158, 482/3, fig. 1350; Regina Shoolman Slatkin, *François Boucher in North American Collections,* National Gallery of Art, Washington, D.C., 1974, p. 109, no. 84, illustrated; Wildenstein and Co., Inc., *François Boucher, A Loan Exhibition for the New York Botanical Garden,* New York, 1980, p. 51, no. 60, fig. 59.

Exhibitions: National Gallery of Art, Washington, D.C., December 1973-March 1974; The Art Institute of Chicago, April 1974-May 1974; Wildenstein and Co., Inc., New York, November 12-December 19, 1980.

65. Jean-Jacques Caffiéri

French, 1725-1792

Study for a River God, 1756

Terra cotta. 16.5 x 16.2 x 11.4 cm. (6-1/2 x 6-3/8 x 4-1/2″) 1971.91
Signed and dated on the back: "fait par J. J. Caffiéri, 1756."

The belief that each river has an attendant deity originated in Greek mythology. River gods probably first appeared in art among the sculptures of the end gables of Greek temples. Customarily located in the narrow triangular ends of the gables, they were always posed in a reclining position, as in the famous sculptures of the Parthenon, Athens and the Temple of Zeus, Olympia.

That the Hyde work represents a river god is certain because of its close relationship to a full length river god by Caffiéri in terra cotta (8-5/8 x 5-7/8″) in the collection of the Yale University Art Gallery.[1] Dated 1757, one year after the Hyde work, it shows the complete figure reclining against an overturned water jug, the standard attribute of river gods. In his extended right arm the Yale example holds an oar, an ancient attribute representing the river Ganges in India. The facial type of the Yale figure, the similar scale, the pose, and such details as the seaweed crown, the fall of the hair, and the musculature of the chest, are precisely those of the Hyde work. The only difference is that the shoulders and chest of the Yale work are undraped.

It appears that Caffiéri made a specialty of the river god theme. It was the subject that he submitted in marble as his acceptance piece to the French Academy in 1759. This was also a bust, and when the Hyde river god was purchased, it was identified by Wildenstein and Company as a study for the marble, though in fact the two works are dissimilar. However, the Hyde bust may reflect an initial acceptance piece design which had been rejected by the Academy.

An exact replica of the Hyde work was sold at Sotheby's in London, July 10, 1975, suggesting that Caffiéri reproduced the subject several times for private collectors.

1. Research by Jane Rehl.

Provenance: David-Weill, Paris; Wildenstein and Co., Inc., New York, c. 1940; purchased from Wildenstein and Co., Inc., 1944.

Literature: Wildenstein and Co., Inc., *French 18th Century Sculptures Formerly of the Collection of David-Weill,* New York, 1940, p. 12, no. 22.

Exhibitions: Wildenstein and Co., Inc., New York, 1940.

66. Jean-Honoré Fragonard

French, 1732-1806

Le Fauçon (The Falcon), c. 1789-1795

Pen and ink with bistre wash on paper. 20.6 x 13.9 cm. (8 x 5-7/16″) 1971.66

Fragonard's design, *Le Fauçon,* illustrates La Fontaine's sentimental tale of the same name.[1] The story involves a falcon, the sole possession of a landed but impoverished Frenchman. The bird was coveted by the young son of a neighboring and well-to-do woman. Ill and dying, the young boy demanded that his mother procure the bird, saying that it was indeed the only thing that could revive him. At first reluctant, the mother, went to her neighbor without immediately revealing her purpose. The neighbor politely offered her a simple repast and she readily accepted. Having no food suitable for so important a guest, the gentleman killed his falcon. Once the dinner was completed, the mother told her host of her dilemma, which was, of course, heightened when she learned that she had just eaten the bird her son had so desired.

It is this scene that Fragonard's drawing illustrates. The shabby interior of the gentleman's humble dwelling is made all the more noticeable by the elegance of his guest who, seated opposite him in the master's chair, is seen throwing up her hands in understandable dismay. Fragonard also updated the seventeenth century tale by outfitting the protagonists in garments fashionable just prior to the Revolution.

In about 1789 the French publisher Pierre Didot began planning a new four-part deluxe edition of La Fontaine's *Contes et Nouvelles.* Each part was to contain twenty engravings designed by Fragonard, which were to be purchased by subscription, volume by volume.[2] Unfortunately Didot's timing was inopportune for so costly a venture, for there was little or no response when the proposed publication was advertised. Presumably in 1789 the buying public was more involved in the political events of revolutionary Paris, and hence, extravagance of this sort would have been out of the question. Whatever the circumstances, Didot altered his plans and only two volumes appeared in 1795, the first containing prints, twenty in all. Of these, sixteen were by Fragonard. The remaining four were engraved after designs by Mallet, Monnet, and Touze, practitioners of the more academic style popular in France at the end of the century. *Le Fauçon* appears as number 15, the image in reverse of that of the drawing.

1. Written by Jane Rehl.
2. Jean de la Fontaine, *Contes et Nouvelles en vers,* à Paris, de l'imprimerie de P. Didot, 1795, I, p. 157, no. 15. In the Musée du Petit Palais, Paris, are a set of fifty-seven drawings by Fragonard illustrating La Fontaine's *Contes et Nouvelles.* Accompanied by a text in carefully executed manuscript form, they closely imitate the composition of Fragonard's drawings for the Didot publication, but in a freer, looser manner. This indicates they were not intended to be copied by an engraver, but rather were created for a collector, as yet unidentified. In date they precede the Hyde drawings.

   Further discussion of Fragonard's various drawings of the fables of La Fontaine occurs in Edwin Wolf's "The Fragonard Plates for the *Contes et Nouvelles,*" *Bulletin of the New York Public Library,* March, 1949, p. 3.

Provenance: David-Weill Collection, Paris, 1928; Wildenstein and Co., Inc., New York; purchased from Wildenstein and Co., Inc., 1942.

Literature: Gabriel Henriot, *Collection David-Weill,* Paris, 1928, III, p. 133, illustrated p. 159; Louis Reau, *Fragonard,* Bruxelles, 1956, p. 226; Alexandre Ananoff, *L'Oeuvre Dessiné de Fragonard,* Paris, 1970, p. 239, no. 2714; Marianne Roland Michel, "Fragonard, Illustrator of the 'Contes' of Fontaine," *Burlington Magazine,* CXII, September-December, 1971, pp. I-VI after p. 716; Denys Sutton, *Fragonard,* National Museum of Western Art, Tokyo, 1980, no. 162, illustrated.

Exhibitions: Wildenstein and Co., Inc., New York, 1938; The National Museum of Western Art, Tokyo, March 18-May 11, 1980; Kyoto Municipal Museum, May 24-June 29, 1980.

67. Josiah Wedgwood

English, 1730-1795

and **John Flaxman**

English, 1755-1826

Portrait of Carl von Linnaeus, 1775-78

Jasperware pottery. 7.3 x 8.2 cm. (2-7/8 x 3-1/4") 1971.291
Signed on back: "WEDGWOOD AND BENTLEY."

In 1775 John Flaxman submitted a bill to Josiah Wedgwood for "Moulding and making a cast from a Medall of Lennaeus." The first documented reference of this being produced in Jasperware was on April 19, 1777. It appeared in the Wedgwood catalogue of 1779.[1]

Wedgwood, of course, was the great English potter, and John Flaxman was to become England's most important sculptor of the period. For twelve years Flaxman worked for Wedgwood, the *Portrait of Linnaeus* being executed in 1775, the first year of his employment. Apparently the work was not an original creation, but it was made from a mold taken from a medal.

Carl von Linnaeus was the Swedish botanist who devised the method of modern botanical classification in his publications *Classes Plantarum* (1738) and *Species Plantarum* (1753). In the portrait he wears the linnea plant that bears his name.

Once Wedgwood molds were made, they could be used almost *ad infinitum.* The rarity and early date of this work can be determined by the stamped signature on the back, "Wedgwood and Bentley"; Thomas Bentley was Wedgwood's partner between 1769-1780. Early Wedgwood may also be identified by the fact that the blue tone is not an applied glaze, but rather it continues through to the back.

The style of the work could be considered eighteenth century French by the very realistic features and by the spontaneously amused and responding expression of the face. It is like the facial types that appear in the terra cottas of the French sculptor Houdon. (In England Louis François Roubiliac was producing similar sculptured portraits.)

Flaxman's own style, as it later evolved, was of a very different sort, a severe neoclassicism, becoming one of the important influences on developing Neoclassicism in Europe.

1. Robin Reilly and George Savage, *Wedgwood Portrait Medallions,* London, 1973, p. 216.

Provenance: Purchased from Ginsburg and Levy, Inc., New York, 1933.

68. Anonymous

French ?

Portrait of a Young Girl, c. 1820

Oil on canvas. 45.7 x 38.1 cm. (18 x 15″) 1971.3

For all of its charm, this portrait of a young girl is a work that provokes more questions than answers. Is it indeed a portrait? The woman looks down not out of the picture, as if the painting may have originally presented some genre theme, and then had been cut down at a subsequent date. It is possible that she once held a letter in her hand, a *billet-doux* so common in French Rococo portrayals of women.

Attributed to Jean-Honoré Fragonard when purchased and once signed at the lower right, it was quickly recog-nized that such an attribution could not be possible; the style has none of Fragonard's strong color or broad brushwork. The false signature was subsequently removed by the art restorer, William Suhr.

The painting has French, English, German, or Swiss characteristics according to the comments of various art historians who have visited The Hyde Collection, though French is the most popular choice. Suggestions have been made that the artist could be anyone from Chardin to early Renoir.

Provenance: Purchased from a "Lausanne family" with arrangements made by a Dr. R. Mermod of Lausanne, Switzerland, 1927.

69. Pierre-Paul Prud'hon

French, 1758-1823

Charles-Hubert Millevoye, c. 1803

Oil on ivory. 16.5 x 13.3 cm. (6-1/2 x 5-1/4″) 1971.35
Signed and dated, right: "P P Prudhon—1803."

The identity of the sitter in this portrait miniature was forgotten when it left the possession of its original owner and entered the collections of those who valued it solely as a painting executed by Prud'hon.[1] It was not until 1880 that the sitter was identified as Charles-Hubert Millevoye, the youthful French poet laureate of the early nineteenth century.[2] The painting itself remained uncatalogued among Prud'hon's work until 1924, when it appeared in Guiffrey's *L'Oeuvre de P.-P. Prud'hon.*[3]

Charles-Hubert Millevoye was born in 1782 in Abbeville, a small town on the Somme River in Northern France. His first major publication came in 1801, a memoir in prose exploring the *Peines et les Plaisirs de l'Imagination* (Pains and Pleasures of the Imagination). Two years later, in 1803, the Lycée de Toulouse honored him with its highest award for his poem *A Mon Ami,* a satire on Parisian life; this marked the beginning of his short but successful career. It was also in this year that Prud'hon painted Millevoye's portrait, which the poet probably presented to his family commemorating his newly achieved fame. Millevoye contracted tuberculosis in 1815 and died the following year at thirty years of age.[4]

Prud'hon's delicate and sensitive handling of this portrait complements the delicate and sensitive nature of its subject. Executed in oils on ivory, the young poet appears to be both proud and vulnerable: proud in his posture, especially in the arms folded just above the waist; and vulnerable in the delicacy of his features, which disclose a certain melancholy in the eyes. Although the portrait is very small, Prud'hon has revealed Millevoye's physiognomy in extraordinary detail: delicate wisps of hair framing a noticeably pallid, but nonetheless appealing face; a sensitive brow and chin, which displays some youthful whiskers; and a prominent nose. His attire is stylish, but informally worn, as the collar of his shirt lies open at the neck in disarray, and his cravat is seen loosely tied below. The intimacy rendered in this miniature is not always characteristic of Prud'hon's portraits and may suggest that the artist had found a certain *esprit d'accord* with Millevoye the man and Millevoye the poet. The small scale, as well as the intimate portrayal, further suggest that Millevoye presented it to his family.

It has often been noted that Prud'hon was an artist caught between two centuries, and certainly this portrait greatly supports the assumption. In scale and intimacy, it can be related to eighteenth century Rococo paintings, while the technique is clearly that of the Neoclassical movement which was initiated by Jacques-Louis David just prior to the French Revolution. Moreover, although Prud'hon presents the poet in a relatively informal way, the exact pose in which the head and torso are symmetrically aligned, indicates further influence from the Neoclassical movement, as does the somber tonality of his palette, relieved only by the delicate color of the cravat. The black background was employed by Prud'hon in other portraits and larger compositions. In this miniature, the darkened background serves to emphasize Millevoye's head, the font of creativity, and at the same time isolates his entire figure from his surroundings. This increases the pervasive air of melancholy, so common among portraits executed during the Romantic movement proper of some twenty years hence.[5]

1. Written by Jane Rehl.
2. Louise Gonse, "Le Portrait de Millevoye par Prud'hon," *Gazette des Beaux-Arts,* 1880, XXI, pp. 239-41, illustrated. Gonse based his identification on an engraving of Millevoye which appeared in the 1812 edition of his *Élégies.*
3. Jean Guiffrey, *L'Oeuvre P.-P. Prud'hon,* Paris, 1924, p. 217, no. 578.
4. One of the better biographies of Millevoye is Alcius Ledieu's *Millevoye, sa Vie et ses Oeuvres,* Paris, 1886.
5. See Joan Siegfried, "The Romantic Artist as Portrait Painter," *Marsyas,* VIII, 1957-9, pp. 30-42, for an analysis of late eighteenth and early nineteenth century portraits.

Provenance: Eugene Tondu, Paris, April 3, 1865; M. Furby, London; M. Charles Bayard, Lyons, 1891; Mrs. H. O. Havermeyer, 1930; The Eighteenth Century Shop, New York ? (purchased at Havermeyer sale); purchased through Valentiner from Freund?

Literature: Gonse, *op. cit.;* Guiffrey, *op. cit.;* Laurence X. Champeau, *The Social Calendar,* New York, March 31, 1930, illustrated only; American Art Association, Anderson Galleries, Inc., *The Estate of Mrs. H. O. Havemeyer, part I, April 10, 1930,* New York, 1930, p. 24, no. 56, illustrated.

70. Jean-Auguste-Dominique Ingres

French, 1780-1867

Study for the Head of Victory, c. 1826-27 and 1866

Oil on canvas, mounted on panel. 23.7 x 18.7 cm. (9-3/8 x 7-3/8") 1971.23
Signed and dated lower right: "Ingres 1866."

In 1826 Ingres received the very important commission from the government of France to execute a painting for the ceiling of the Salle Clarac, a room in a new addition to the old palace of the Louvre.[1] Ingres himself was to devise the subject. Basing his ideas on Raphael's famous *School of Athens* (Vatican, Rome), he composed a subject, the *Apotheosis of Homer,*[2] which shows the winged victory crowning the blind poet with a laurel wreath. Around him are assembled forty-six men and women from ancient and modern history who had achieved distinction in the arts and sciences. Below Homer, to the right and left, are seated two female allegorical figures representing Homer's two epic poems, the *Iliad* and the *Odyssey.*

In The Hyde Collection are two of Ingres' oil studies for the figures of Victory and the Odyssey. Both once belonged to the painter Degas; both are also rough fragments cut from a larger canvas, probably of many studies; and remounted at some subsequent time, presumably around 1866, the date on the *Victory* study. Both fragments were then completed by further painting. The top of the head of Victory and her bust are later additions. In these additions a slight change of style occurs. While it seems probable that the additions were executed by Ingres since both studies were sold in 1866, they may have been the work of a later hand, possibly even the hand of Degas who had owned the paintings.

Although the date 1866 appears on the Hyde *Victory* on the lower addition to the original fragment, it is suggested here that the study was executed in 1826 for the final painted version of 1827. While the Hyde *Victory* appears significantly altered in the final painting, where she turns completely towards Homer, her exact positioning in the Hyde study, head turning away and to the right of her torso, can be observed in an early compositional drawing, presumably from 1826.[3]

Particular features of the face, especially the dark eyebrows and the wide jaw, indicate that this study was taken from a living model, perhaps Ingres' cousin Mme. de Lauréal, as suggested by Georges Wildenstein,[4] because of its similarity to Ingres' portrait of her sketched in oil around 1821.[5] Both the heads of the Victory and of the Odyssey were somewhat idealized in the final work, which is in accord with the classical character of the *Apotheosis of Homer* theme.

1. Research by Jane Rehl.
2. In 1855 the final painting was removed from the ceiling of the Louvre. It was shown at the Exposition Universelle in Paris and at the Musée du Luxembourg, where it remained to 1874. Today the painting hangs on the Louvre walls, while a copy is on the ceiling of the Salle Clarac.
3. Norman Schelenoff, *Ingres, Ses Sources Litteraires,* Paris, 1956, pl. XXIII.
4. Georges Wildenstein, *Ingres,* New York, 1956, p. 204, no. 201, fig. 126.
5. Although this portrait bears the date 1840, the date is not Ingres', according to Daniel Ternois, who dates it to about 1821 or earlier. Daniel Ternois, "Ingres et son Temps," *Inventaire des Collections Publiques Françaises. Montauban, Musée* Ingres. Paris, 1965, no. 162.

Provenance: Anonymous sale (by Ingres?), March 21, 1866, lot 72; M. L. . . . Paris, Hotel Drouot, May 14, 1873, lot 38; Edgar Degas, Paris, March 26-27, 1918, lot 62; Henri Lapauze, Paris, June 21, 1929, lot 58; anonymous sale, June 14, 1930, lot 25, Paris; E. and A. Milch, Inc., New York; purchased from E. and A. Milch, Inc., 1931.

Literature: Hôtel Drouot, Paris *Tableaux Modernes, Dessins et Aquarelles, Collection de M. L.,* Paris, May 14, 1873, p. 11, lot 38; Galerie Georges Petit, *Catalogue des Tableaux Modernes et Anciens . . . Composant la Collection Edgar Degas,* Paris, March 26, 27, 1918, p. 28, lot 62; Hôtel Drouot, *Catalogue des Tableaux et Dessins par J. A. D. Ingres, Composant la Collection Henry Lapauze,* Paris, June 21, 1929, p. 39, lot 58, illustrated; Georges Wildenstein, *Ingres,* New York, 1956, p. 232, no. 323, fig. 99; S. Lane Faison, Jr., *Art Tours and Detours in New York State,* New York, 1964, p. 115, fig. 193; Daniel Ternois and Ettore Camesasca, *L'Opera Completa di Ingres,* Milan, 1968, p. 105, no. 120n, illustrated p. 104, French ed., Paris, 1971.

Exhibitions: M. Knoedler and Co., New York, 1939; Museum of Fine Arts, Springfield, 1939; Cincinnati Art Museum, 1940.

71. Jean-Auguste-Dominique Ingres

French, 1780-1867

Study for the Odyssey, c. 1826-27 and 1866

Oil on canvas mounted on panel. 23.7 x 18.7 cm. (9-7/16 x 7-3/8″) 1971.25

The *Odyssey,* like number 70 in this collection, is a study for the *Apotheosis of Homer,* a painting commissioned from Ingres by the French government in 1826.[1] In the center of the painting Homer is shown enthroned. To his left and slightly below is seated a female figure representing his epic poem the *Odyssey.* To his right sits a similar heroic woman representing the *Iliad.* In the final painting, the figure of the *Odyssey* is differently posed and dressed from her appearance in the Hyde study. Instead of a Greek costume, the figure is swathed in an all-encompassing robe. Her left arm encircles her waist, while her right hand is under her chin, palm up. The pose of the Hyde *Odyssey,* left hand to brow, does appear in a preliminary drawing study for the *Apotheosis of Homer* composition,[2] and thus may be dated before the final painting, which was completed in 1827. Around 1850 Ingres used the exact pose of the Hyde *Odyssey* in a single painting of the figure of the *Odyssey* (Lyons, France).[3] In this figure an oar, her attribute, is held in the right hand. On her head she wears a Greek helmet, the one significant change from the Hyde study.

The Hyde's *Odyssey* study, like its companion, *Study for the Head of Victory,* was once cut from a larger canvas and remounted on a new canvas with later additions made to complete the figure. These additions include the top of the head, all the chest below the base of the neck, and the lower part of the arm. Perhaps Ingres himself did this to prepare these studies for his sale of 1866. (Both the *Odyssey* and the *Head of Victory* are the same size.) Possibly, also, these were sold as fragments. As with the *Victory* study, it is feasible that Edgar Degas himself, a later owner, remounted and made the additions to the painting. This is suggested by the slight differences in style which appear between the later and the earlier work on the canvas.

1. Research by Jane Rehl.
2. Norman Schelenoff, *Ingres, Ses Sources Litteraires,* Paris, 1956, pl. XXIII.
3. Georges Wildenstein, *Ingres,* New York, 1956, no. 182, fig. 106.

Provenance: Anonymous sale (by Ingres?), March 21, 1866; Haro, Paris, May 30-31, 1892, lot 108; G.-H. Edgar Degas, Paris, March 26-27, 1918, lot 67; Henri Lapauze, Paris, June 21, 1929, lot 57, to Baron Fukushima; purchased from E. and A. Milch, Co., Inc., New York, 1929. (In these sales the painting was consistently mistitled as the *Iliad.*)

Literature: Degas sale, *op. cit.,* p. 30; Lapauze sale, *op. cit.,* p. 38 (as *Iliad*); Jean Alazard, *Ingres et L'Ingrisme,* Paris, 1950, pl. LVIII; Georges Wildenstein, *Ingres,* New York, 1956, p. 202, no. 183, fig. 108; Daniel Ternois and Ettore Camesasca, *L'Opera Completa di Ingres,* Milan, 1968, p. 105, no. 120 dd, illustrated, p. 104, (French ed., Paris, 1971).

Exhibitions: Kraushaar, New York, 1929; M. Knoedler and Co., New York, 1939; Museum of Fine Arts, Springfield, 1939; Cincinnati Art Museum, 1940.

72. Jean-Auguste-Dominique Ingres

French, 1780-1867

Paolo and Francesca, c. 1855-60

Oil on canvas. 28.3 x 22.2 cm. (11-1/2 x 8-3/4″) 1971.24

The story of Paolo and Francesca is from Dante's *Inferno,* Canto V. Paolo Malatesta and Francesca da Rimini are bound together for eternity in Circle 2 of Hell. Francesca was the young and beautiful bride of Giovanni Malatesta, a powerful and brave soldier, but lame and quite ugly. Her only solace in what had been an arranged marriage was her innocent relationship with Giovanni's brother Paolo, with whom she shared a love of literature. One day as they read together the story of Sir Lancelot and Queen Guinevere, they became overwhelmed by their passion for each other, and Paolo "breathed on (her) lips the tremor of his kiss." This is the moment of the story portrayed by Ingres in this painting. But a moment later Giovanni, who had seen them kiss, rushed in and killed his wife and brother with his sword.[1]

Ingres, who was quite taken with this subject, executed no less than six versions of it, the first two being in 1814, the last in 1856-57.[2] While the Hyde *Paolo and Francesca* is inscribed by a later hand on the back "1819 Francesca da Rimini par Ingres," it is proposed here that the painting be dated 1855-60.[3]

In composition the Hyde version is closely related to the painting of 1856-57 (now disappeared), with Paolo located to Francesca's right, rather than to her left as in all the other versions. In both, the figure of the angered husband drawing his sword is absent. In accord with the new emphasis on the sentimental theme of the lovers' first (and last) kiss, the figures are brought forward and the space reduced, achieving greater intimacy in the impression.

Stylistically similar to the Hyde painting is the only one of the series actually dated by Ingres; *Paolo and Francesca* (Turpin de Crissé Museum, Angers). But it is known that Ingres in his maturity was embarrassed by his style before 1824 because of its conscious archaicizing; consequently, he may have followed in this instance his common practice of reworking an early canvas that had remained in his possession. He would have done this to prepare the painting for a major exhibition of his work at the *Exposition Universelle* of 1855. But this possible reworking of the earlier canvas would account for similarities in style between a painting seemingly early with its 1819 date and the Hyde version with its proposed date of 1855-60. The late dating of the Hyde work is further indicated by the fact that it was the only painting Ingres chose to exhibit in the *Exposition de Tableaux de l'Ecole Moderne* of 1860. It is suggested here that the great popularity of the Angers version, exhibited in 1855, caused Ingres to develop two more versions of the theme, but of a necessarily different format. While it was Ingres' custom to repeat in a number of paintings subjects that had become favorites, no two of these would ever be alike. The most significant change in the Hyde version and the related work of 1855-57 would be the absence of the angry husband in the background, with the emphasis placed rather, on Paolo's tentative first kiss.

1. Research and conclusions by Jane Rehl.
2. The two 1814 versions are in the Musée Condé, Chantilly, and the Barber Institute of Fine Arts, Birmingham, England; Wildenstein 100, 123. An 1819 version is at the Musée Turpin de Crissé, Angers, Wildenstein 121; an 1845 version at the Musée Bonnat, Bayonne, Wildenstein 249. The version considered by Wildenstein to be the latest (1856-57) was sold in London in 1966 and cannot at present be located; Wildenstein 282. For complete references to Wildenstein's catalogue see Literature below.
3. The painting is dated 1819-20 by Georges Wildenstein, and c. 1845 by Camesasca and Ternois (see Literature below).

Provenance: Vicomte du Tallis, 1860; sold May 2, 1865; purchased from Dr. Mermod, Lausanne, Switzerland, 1923.

Literature: Henri Delaborde, *Ingres,* Paris, 1870, p. 224; Georges Wildenstein, *Ingres,* Paris, 1954, p. 186, no. 122, fig. 70; Accademia di Francia, Villa Medici, Rome, *Ingres in Italia,* p. 122; Daniel Ternois and Eltore Camesasca, *L'Opera Completa di Ingres,* Milan, 1968, p. 112, no. 140, fig. 140a, French ed., Paris, 1971; Melinda Curtis, University of Maryland Art Gallery, *Search for Innocence,* College Park, 1975, p. 82, no. 13, fig. 10, illustrated in reverse.

Exhibitions: Exposition des Tableaux de l'Ecole Moderne, 26 Boulevard des Italiens, Paris, 1860; Museum of Fine Arts, Springfield, 1939; M. Knoedler and Co., Inc., New York, 1940; Cincinnati Art Museum; University of Maryland Art Gallery, College Park, 1975.

73. Joseph Mallard William Turner

English, 1775-1851

Grand Canal, Venice, c. 1840

Watercolor, pastel, and gouache on paper. 50.2 x 73.7 cm. (19-3/4 x 29″) 1971.51

The view is of the Dogano da Mar, the customs house of Venice. Behind the Dogano the two domes of Santa Maria del Salute stand against the sky. On the right of the Dogano opens the mouth of the Grand Canal, and on the left is the canal of Guidecca. Thus the traditional title of this work is not precisely correct. The view is taken from the north side of the broad canal of St. Mark, possibly from the quay of the Piazza di San Marco. To the right on the shore line, not visible in the painting, would be the Piazza and Cathedral of St. Mark and the Europa Hotel, where Turner stayed while in Venice.

Among scholars the dating of Turner's work is still an uncertain subject, but the style of the Hyde painting seems quite similar to other works executed by Turner in Venice in 1840. While Turner usually sketched from nature only with a pencil, on the occasion of this Venetian visit, he painted in front of the actual scene on large sheets of paper with watercolor and gouache.

However, in its vaguely defined forms, dissolving in light and mist, the Venice that appears here is more a city of the mind than it is a topographical survey. It is Venice perceived in a dream-like reverie. In that it is characteristic of one aspect of nineteenth century romantic painting.

Often condemned in his own time for the unclear definition of his forms, Turner is now recognized as one of the precursors of the modern art movement. He described this indistinctness in his art as a means of endowing his form with a "mysterious doubt." In the Hyde painting, shapes may still be recognized and the scene identified, but these shapes may be perceived as trembling on the verge of dissolution. Such vagueness in art frees the spectator's mind to experience a rich variety of feelings; by contrast, tightly rendered forms hold the mind to a close and narrow path.

Turner has often been called an Impressionist. Like the later French Impressionists whom he influenced, he was a student of color theory and actively sought to discern the true hues that vibrate in a natural setting. But he was not a true Impressionist in that he was not interested in making a scientific record of nature's changing colored lights. Rather, his palette remained relatively constant, a development more of his inner artistic consciousness than of the observed natural scene. A variety of yellows prevail in most of his artistic renderings, with blue breaking through at intervals. Red will appear, but only as a flash of color restricted to small areas.

Turner's primary artistic medium was transparent watercolor. Later he added the more opaque gouache. By doing so, he was able to achieve in watercolor something of the texture of oil paint. At the same time his fully developed oil technique seemed to be a natural consequence of his earlier handling of watercolor.

Provenance: The Hyde Archives contain no receipt for the purchase of this painting. An old photograph of the work is stamped "Bernès, Marouteau & Cie., Photographes, 36, Avenue de Chatillon, Paris."

74. Hilaire Germain Edgar Degas

French, 1834-1917

Mlle. Marguerite Degas (Mme. Fevre), c. 1856

Pencil on paper. 20.7 x 13.2 cm. (8-1/8 x 5-1/2″) 1971.64
Collector's mark, lower left, of Marcel Guérin.
Paper impressed, upper left: "E C"; lower left: "Lundi, Mercredi, Vendredi; de 1Heure à 3 Hres."
Inscribed in pencil on verso: "Portrait de Mm. Fevre (Marguerite Degas)
acheté a Henri Févre (son fils) a Nice."

The portrait is of Marguerite Degas, the younger of Degas' two sisters. She faces directly forward. Around her head appear the faint outlines of what has been identified as a morning bonnet. In the Louvre, Paris, is a three-quarter length portrait of Mlle. Degas, facing directly out, and dressed in morning dress and bonnet. The Louvre portrait has been dated 1859-60.[1] At least six other drawings and an oil study exist of Mlle. Degas that are related to the portrait in the Louvre. It is proposed here that these belong to the period shortly after Degas' return from a trip to Italy in 1859, while the Hyde drawing dates from the period just before the artist left for Italy in 1856.[2] The Hyde portrait is different from the others in both medium and style. It is in pencil; the others are in black chalk or charcoal. In the Hyde drawing forms are delicately suggested, a reflection of how much Degas was influenced by Ingres' drawings at this time. The later drawings are comparatively heavy in treatment, with more explicit forms. Further-more, the Hyde drawing resembles other family portraits which were executed by Degas in 1855-56, particularly in the distant facial expressions, an aloofness of manner the artist had learned from the portraits of the Italian Mannerist painter Bronzino. Examples are the portraits that Degas did of his brothers René (Smith College Museum of Art, Northampton, Mass.) and Achille (National Gallery of Art, Washington, D.C.).

Marguerite Degas married the architect Henri Fevre in 1865. Because the headdress in the Hyde drawing had been misinterpreted to be a form of bonnet worn in weddings of the period, the drawing was associated with Marguerite's wedding and was given the improbable late date of 1865. Sometime after 1867 she went with her husband to Buenos Aires. After her death in 1895 Degas sent several of his drawings of Marguerite to her children. That the Hyde drawing was among this group is suggested by the fact that it once belonged to Henri Fevre, Marguerite's son.

1. Paul-André Lemoisne, *Degas et son oeuvre,* Paris, 1946, I, p. 37. It is Lemoisne who identified the costume.
2. Research and conclusions by Jane Rehl.

Provenance: Henri Fevre, the artist's nephew. Marcel Guérin. (Guérin wrote the catalogue for the *Exposition Degas,* Galerie Georges Petit, Paris, 1924.); purchased from Wildenstein and Co., Inc., 1951.

75. Hilaire Germain Edgar Degas

French, 1834-1917

Dancer with Red Stockings, c. 1883-85

Pastel on paper. 75.9 x 58.7 cm. (29-7/8 x 23-1/8″) 1971.65
Signed lower right: "Degas."

Seated, a young female dancer draws on a footless stocking, one of a pair of the leg-warmers customarily worn by dancers during or after vigorous activity.[1] Her body appears flushed and faintly damp with perspiration as if she had just finished dancing. In contrast, a less completely drawn dancer is seated beside her in a hunched over position with her hands thrust beneath her folded arms. This is a typical pose of someone shivering from the cold. Apparently she is waiting to perform. Thus the artist presents a content more definite than what would normally be expected from an Impressionist work.

The drawing is rapidly executed, with many *pentimenti,* particularly in the rendering of the legs of the figures, thus it is apparent that the artist executed the pastel on the scene. There is the authenticity and immediacy of effect that is a general characteristic of the Impressionist style.

This sense of immediacy is equally effected by Degas' composition, wherein the seated dancers are portrayed from a high perspective angle, as they would have appeared to Degas as he stood above them and from a position slightly to their right. Such a viewpoint implies an accidental quality, a sense of the casual way things are perceived in normal experience. The resulting composition with the angling of the floorboards beneath the dancers' feet, resembles compositions of Japanese prints and contemporary French photography, which both strongly influenced Degas with their illustration of temporal or momentary images. The unequal massing of the forms and their close proximity to the border of this sketch to produce the suggestion of a flat pattern, further indicate the influence of the Japanese print.

Degas began to observe and actively portray ballet subjects in 1872 and continued with ballet themes to the end of his life. As a subject, the ballet lent itself to Degas' particular artistic concerns—movement, light, color, and surface design. His first compositions depicted relatively large ballet classes and stage rehearsals in deep and dramatic spaces. As his style evolved, his designs became simpler with close views of fewer dancers. Lemoisne dates the Hyde drawing c. 1883-85,[2] in accord with other compositions of this short-lived expressive phase in Degas' career.

1. Initial research by Jane Rehl.
2. Paul-André Lemoisne, *Degas et son oeuvre,* Paris, 1946, III, no. 760.

Provenance: Ernest Chausson, Paris. Musician and composer, and friend of Degas, Chausson acquired the drawing directly from the artist; sold by Mme. Chausson, Hôtel Drouot, Paris, June 5, 1936; Lord Ivor Spencer Churchill according to Lillian Browse (see Literature below); no records of purchase or sale. Paul Rosenberg, New York; purchased 1944.

Literature: Paul Lafond, *Degas,* Paris, 1919, II, illustrated in color pp. 24-25; Paul-André Lemoisne, *op. cit.;* Lillian Browse, *Degas Dancers,* London, 1949, p. 407, no. 222, illustrated; S. Lane Faison, Jr., *Art Tours and Detours in New York State,* New York, 1964, p. 116, fig. 194.

Exhibitions: Brussels, Palais de Beaux-Arts, 1935; Musée de l'Orangerie, 1937.

76. Hilaire Germain Edgar Degas

French, 1834-1917

Draught Horse, c. 1881

Hollow-cast bronze. 16.5 x 13.3 x 21.5 cm. (6-1/2 x 5-1/4 x 8-1/2") 1971.92
Inscribed, to right of front leg: "Degas";
stamped on pedestal left rear: "cire perdu A A Hébrard Paris B-13."

Degas' *Draught Horse* was at one time thought to be a preliminary study for the horse that appears in his *Mlle. Fiocre dans le ballet "La Source"* (The Brooklyn Museum), a painting he completed around 1867. However, according to the most recent study of Degas' extant sculptural oeuvre by Charles Millard, the *Draught Horse* has been placed at the very beginning of a series of equine models dated 1881-1890 by Millard. These are all apparently quite independent of any painting compositions.[1] It is Millard's conclusion that Degas sculpted a series of horses in the 1880's as a result of the direct influence of Eadweard Muybridge's photographs of horses in action. These photographs were published in the French periodical *La Nature* in 1878. Whatever its inspiration, Degas' *Draught Horse* appears to be one of his earliest sculptured horses, because of its relative lack of movement, the way the form acts only in a single plane, and because of its unfinished texture. His later horses are more active and three-dimensional.[2]

In the *Draught Horse* it is apparent that a direct study of the horse was made. This becomes obvious particularly in the legs, where the tendons, muscle, and bone structure were executed with knowledgeable detail.

During his lifetime Degas exhibited only one sculpture, the *Fourteen Year Old Ballet Dancer,* at the Impressionist Exhibition of 1881. After the artist's death in 1918 more than one hundred and fifty small models in wax of horses, dancers, and other figures were found in his studio. Almost immediately the Degas family approached A. A. Hébrard to see if these could be cast in bronze. By 1919 the project was underway. In charge was Hébrard's master founder Albino Palazzolo. Of the surviving sculptures it was determined that only seventy-three could withstand the casting process, although Palazzolo had developed a technique which could preserve the original model.

Twenty-three sets of each piece were cast; one set for Hébrard; one for Degas' heirs; a master set, and the remaining twenty to be sold. Those to be sold can be distinguished by a casting code which is indicated by a letter from A through T, the alphabetical sequence indicating the sequence in which the works were cast. In addition, a number from one through seventy-three was assigned to each of the seventy-three models. The Hyde Collection's *Draught Horse* has the code number B-13.

Of the castings that were not to be sold, each example of the master set is marked by the word "modèle." Each sculpture to go to the heirs was marked by the code "Her D" or simply "Her." The founder Hébrard's own set can be recognized by an absence of any marks but the founder's name.[3]

1. Charles W. Millard, *The Sculpture of Edgar Degas,* Princeton, 1976, p. 23, no. 83.
2. Research and observations by Jane Rehl.
3. Jean Adhémar, "Before the Degas Bronzes," *Art News,* November 1955, p. 70.

Provenance: Halvorsen, collector and dealer, apparently purchased the entire "B" series; acquired from Halvorsen by Feragil, New York; purchased from Feragil, November 1925.

Literature: (the references are to other castings) John Rewald, "Degas' Dancers and Horses," *Art News,* October 15, 1944, p. 23; John Rewald, Foreword, *Edgar Degas, Original Wax Sculptures,* M. Knoedler and Co., Inc., 1955, no. 2; John Rewald, *Degas Works in Sculpture, A Complete Catalogue,* New York, 1957, VII, fig. 59; Michele Beaulieu, "Les Sculptures de Degas, Essai de Chronologie," *Revue du Louvre et des Musées de France,* V, 19, 1969, pp. 370-371; Charles Millard, *The Sculpture of Edgar Degas,* Princeton, 1976, pp. 5, 6, 20, 97, 100, fig. 9.

77. Hilaire Germain Edgar Degas

French, 1834-1917

Dancer Tying Her Scarf, c. 1887

Black crayon heightened with white on paper squared for transfer.
47.3 x 30.2 cm. (18-5/8 x 11-5/8″) 1971.63
Stamp of the Degas Sale lower left: "Degas."

This figure study by Degas was used by the artist in two larger oil compositions, *Danseuses au Foyer (la Contre Contrebasse)* (The Detroit Institute of Art), and *Dans la Salle de Danse, Frise* (Hammond Collection, Santa Barbara).[1] To facilitate the transfer of the image to another surface, the artist followed the traditional technique of dividing the surface by a grid. Presumably a similar grid lies beneath the surface of the painting at Detroit. In the Detroit oil the dancer fastening her scarf is to the right foreground of the picture. Beside her in the center, two other figures tie on their ballet slippers. In the background of this relatively deep picture space, other dancers are shown practicing. None of the faces of these figures are visible. Degas had reached a point in his development during the 1880's where the human figure was depersonalized. Instead, the human form with its varied poses had become primarily a source for compositional patterns.

The painting in Detroit is dated by Lemoisne c. 1887.[1] The Hyde drawing most probably could be dated at the same time.

1. Paul-André Lemoisne, *Degas et son oeuvre,* Paris, 1946, III, no. 900, IV, pp. 139-42. Lillian Browse, *Degas Dancers,* London, 1949, 120, 120a. Initial research by Jane Rehl.

Provenance: Degas sale, Paris, 1918, sale II, no. 351.

Literature: Galerie Georges Petit, Paris, *Catalogue des Tableaux, Pastels et Dessins par Edgar Degas,* sale II, p. 198, no. 351, illustrated; Lillian Browse, *op. cit.,* p. 379, no. 121, illustrated.

78. Camille Pissarro

French, 1830-1903

Sous-Bois (In the Woods), 1862

Black chalk and white lead on brown paper. 24 x 18.4 cm. (9-7/16 x 7-1/4″) 1971.77
Signed and dated in chalk lower left: "C. Pissarro 1862"; inscribed in pen lower right: "à mon cousin Lucien Cardore."

While the dedication "à mon cousin Lucien Cardore" is quite legible, the name "Cardore" does not seem to appear in any of the Pissarro literature, including Kathleen Adler's recent biography (St. Martin's Press, New York, 1978). When Pissarro's son was born in 1863, he was called "Lucien," a name absent from Adler's genealogy chart. Did Pissarro name his son after the mysterious Lucien Cardore?

The drawing, probably a road in the forest of Montmorency, was executed early in Pissarro's career while he was still under the influence of the famous Barbizon painter Camille Corot. Though he had met Monet in 1859 (and Cézanne in 1861), the future Impressionists had yet to coalesce as a group and develop their characteristic style. The closed forest scene is still in the manner of the Barbizon School. The vertical format, tall delicate trees, and blurred foliage, are a reflection of Corot's style. However, the road plunging directly back from the center is a favorite compositional device that remained throughout Pissarro's career. Here the source may be seventeenth century Dutch. Both Jacob van Ruisdael and Meindert Hobbema executed such compositions. But the logic of presenting a scene from the most normal human point of view, in this case the point of view of a person standing on a wooded road, is an approach to landscape that the later Impressionists derived from the style of another Barbizon painter, Charles-François Daubigny.

The Hyde drawing reflects Corot's blend of naturalism and romanticism, though just in 1862, Pissarro was on the point of casting off that vestigial romanticism. In that year he began to paint simple, unpicturesque open fields and views of ordinary country towns. The Hyde drawing is closer in composition to an earlier work, his *Picnic at Montmorency* of 1858.[1] It was in 1858 that Pissarro moved to the town of Montmorency, which is on the southeast edge of the Forest of Montmorency, about eleven miles from Paris.

1. Ludovic-Rodo Pissarro and Lionello Venturi, *Camille Pissarro, son art-son oeuvre,* P. Rosenberg, Paris, 1939, no. 12, p. 79, illustrated II, pl. B.

Provenance: Originally from the collection of the Impressionist's dealer Durand-Ruel, the work was referred to by Rewald in 1946 as from a "private collection, England."

Literature: A. Tabarant, *Pissarro,* Paris, 1924, pl. 2; John Rewald, The Museum of Modern Art, *The History of Impressionism,* New York, 1946, illustrated p. 71; Maria and Godfrey Blunden, *Impressionists and Impressionism,* Geneva, 1970, p. 77, illustrated; *Monet and Impressionism,* XVII (from the series *Grand Collection of French Art*), Tokyo, 1975, no. 64, illustrated.

79. Gustave Courbet

French, 1819-1877

Waterfall Near Ornans, c. 1865

Oil on canvas. 40 x 54.3 cm. (15-7/8 x 21-3/8") 1971.13
Signed lower left: "G. Courbet."

The *Waterfall Near Ornans* probably belongs with the series of landscape paintings done by Courbet during a visit to his family home at Ornans in 1865. In these same years he was working closely with the young Impressionists, particularly Monet and Whistler. In their mutual concern with determining scientific facts about how the eye perceives nature, the Impressionists at this time had arrived at the gray-green tonality we see in the *Waterfall Near Ornans.* Following contemporary color theory, Courbet and the Impressionists believed that the scattered colors in a scene tend toward a neutral gray when mixed in the spectators' eye, much like the effect of a spinning color-wheel.

Provenance: Charles Wuester, Paris; purchased from Roland Balaij, 1939.

Courbet was the founder of the Realist movement in French art. The realism of his early style had to do with subject matter. Around 1850 he achieved a degree of public notoriety for his down-to-earth portrayals of real life in his *Burial at Ornans* (Louvre, Paris), a peasant funeral, and his *Stone-Breakers* (destroyed), a painting of two laborers working on a road. But after 1856 his definition of realism seems to have shifted to what became the Impressionist position, to make an exact record of how the eye sees. From that point most of his paintings are of seascapes and landscapes, in spite of the fact that history remembers Courbet as a painter of the human figure.

80. Pierre-Auguste Renoir

French, 1841-1919

Estelle in a Red Hat, 1876

Oil on canvas. 40.9 x 32.6 cm. (16-1/8 x 12-7/8″) 1971.39
Signed in monogram lower left: "A.R."

Ambroise Vollard, who originally owned this painting, identified the sitter as a girl named Estelle. Estelle and her sister Jeanne both modeled for Renoir during 1876 while he was painting the *Moulin de la Galette,* one of his major works (Louvre, Paris). The girls would appear to have been prostitutes Renoir met at the Moulin de la Galette, a popular out-door dance hall in Paris. Estelle appears in the famous painting, seated at the table in the foreground and wearing the same striped dress. What little we know about her is recorded in a conversation with Vollard.[1]

Estelle in a Red Hat was painted during that short time in Renoir's career when he could be classified as an Impressionist. The broad brushwork and bright colors resemble the Impressionist technique, though the work is not truly Impressionist in style. If the style of Monet with its almost scientific concern for the reflected light of visible reality is true Impressionism, then Renoir's painting would not fit the definition. In his concept the girl comes first; his bias lies with his subject matter. The Impressionist color becomes merely a means to decorate the model in an attractive way, as Renoir at the start of his career decorated china with painted flowers.

At this period in his development, most of Renoir's female subjects are clad in contemporary costume, consistent with the realism required by Impressionist doctrine. In theory at least, the subject matter of Monet, Degas, Sisley, and Pissarro was taken directly from usual experiences and were devoid of artistic artificiality.

1. Ambroise Vollard, *Renoir, an Intimate Record,* New York, 1925, p. 75.

Provenance: There is conflict between sources; when purchased in 1940 from the Lilienfeld Galleries, New York, the information supplied was that, "The painting was bought from Renoir by a friend, M. Leclanche." It was in the possession of the Galeries Bernheim-Jeune, then the collector Alphonse Kahn. It was apparently owned by the Carroll Carstairs Gallery, New York in the later 1930s where it appeared in an exhibition entitled "Femmes et Fleurs." But in Daulte (see Literature) collections listed are Ambroise Vollard, Paris, and Galerie Druet, Paris.

Literature: Ambroise Vollard, *Tableaux, Pastels et Dessins de Pierre-Auguste Renoir,* 1918, II, p. 113, illustrated; *Art Digest,* XIV, January 1, 1940, illustrated p. 13; Françoise Daulte, *Auguste Renoir: Catalogue Raisonné,* Lausanne, 1971, no. 206, illustrated.

Exhibitions: Carroll Carstairs Gallery, New York, "Femmes et Fleurs," late 1930's.

81. Pierre-Auguste Renoir

French, 1841-1919

Coco, 1905

Oil on canvas. 27.7 x 36 cm. (10-7/8 x 14-3/16″) 1971.38
Signed upper right: "Renoir."

Represented is Renoir's son Claude, called "Coco," who was born August 14, 1901, when Renoir was sixty years old. Completely enamored with his son, Coco became one of the artist's favorite subjects in this period of his life. The child is represented in exactly this pose in at least two other works. The version in the collection of the Barnes Foundation, Merion, Pennsylvania, shows a woman who appears to be Gabrielle, seated behind him with her right arm in a position similar to Coco's, as if she were instructing the child how to write for the first time. In a version illustrated in Paul André's *Renoir,* Gabrielle is dressed in a different costume, and her right arm supports her head as she watches Coco's attempt to write.[1] (Gabrielle, the niece of Renoir's wife, had joined the family in 1893 as a servant and became one of the artist's favorite models.)

While art historians still classify Renoir as an Impressionist because of his association with the original Impressionist movement, he was in fact, never a total Impressionist, for he never adopted Monet's painting of light as an end in itself. Renoir's deep engagement in his subject and his later concern with form (shape) over color would make him more what is considered to be a Post-Impressionist, more closely related artistically to Gauguin than to Monet.

At the time Renoir painted *Coco,* his art had focused almost entirely upon the rendering of a particular kind of round-faced, round-bodied female form. Renoir followed this preconceived facial and body type, even when his model was a specific person. Thus, even in this portrait of his son Coco, Renoir must have sacrificed individual characteristics to his established conventional type. Coco's face is like that of the young girls of most of his later art. If other clearly identified portraits of Coco did not survive, it could be assumed that this was a portrait not of a boy, but rather of a girl. This would seem to suggest that even in life, Renoir would have liked his children to conform to his mental notion of ideal humanity which was predicated on a particular female type.

The painting technique is as characteristic of his style as is the subject. The dominant tonality of all his later works is this earthy red color, which upon close inspection, appears not dull at all since it is produced by many layers of translucent paint representing a variety of reds. Consistent with the simplicity of the overall form, the brushwork is simplicity itself, following a few basic directional currents.

1. Paul André, *Renoir,* Paris, 1928, pl. 67.

Provenance: Purchased from Lilienfeld Galleries, New York, 1948. In a note to Mrs. Hyde, Karl Lilienfeld wrote that the previous owner did not wish to be identified. Elsewhere he records that the original owner was "Durand-Ruel." Paul Durand-Ruel was the art dealer who originally supported the Impressionists. He and his family became close to Renoir. Paul Durand-Ruel's grandson Charles was a close friend of Coco. But it may be assumed that the painting came from the Durand-Ruel Gallery and not from the private collection of the family.

Exhibitions: Dalzell Hatfield Galleries, Ambassador Hotel, Los Angeles, July 25 to September 15 (no year given), illustrated.

82. Georges Seurat

French, 1859-1891

Banks of the Seine near Courbevoie, 1883

Oil on wooden panel. 15.8 x 24.9 cm. (6-7/32 x 9-13/16″) 1971.45

This small panel seems certainly to be one of Seurat's many studies in oil for what was to be his first major painting, *Bathers on the Banks of the Seine at Asnières,* 1883-84 (Tate Gallery, London).[1] In the background of the final painting in the Tate, appear the bridge and factories of Courbevoie, the town mentioned in the title of the Hyde painting. The Hyde composition is essentially that of the larger *Bathers* but without the figures. On the left is the bank of the Seine River. If the viewer is facing Courbevoie from Asnières, the block of trees on the right may well be a part of the Island of the Grande Jatte, the setting for Seurat's masterpiece, *Sunday Afternoon on the Grande Jatte,* 1886 (The Art Institute of Chicago). As in the large *Bathers,* architecture and what may be a bridge terminate the picture space in the middle distance. This study and the final painting were probably executed on the Paris side of the Seine, since a green belt, the Quai Michelet, has always existed on this bank of the river. On the other side, streets run directly along the edge of the river.

Courbevoie is situated on the Seine River on a line west and slightly north of Paris, approximately five miles from the Louvre. The main road from Courbevoie to Paris, today called the Boulevard de Verdun, cuts across the center of the Island of the Grande Jatte.

The style of the Hyde painting is close to that of the other studies for the *Bathers on the Banks of the Seine at Asnières,* resembling almost exactly that of the *Horses in the Water* in the collection of Cristabel, Lady Aberconway, London.[2] While C. M. de Hauke (see Literature) lists only fourteen oil studies related specifically to the *Bathers,* in fact, this composition and the one cited above, must be considered satellites of the major work because of similarities in arrangement.

Seurat is famous as founder of the Post-Impressionist movement known as Pointillism (a term which he did not like). In this movement the Impressionist manner of representing the reflected colored lights scattered through nature is reduced to a precise system, governed by a rational color theory, and rendered in paint applied almost mechanically to the canvas surface in small dots. However, the oil study under consideration precedes Seurat's fully developed Pointillism, and comes at an earlier, more Impressionist phase of the artist's career. The brush strokes are varied to suggest the different qualities of light reflected from different kinds of objects. In the foliage short strokes are criss-crossed at an angle to each other. In the water they are horizontal and parallel to each other, but in the sky the paint appears to follow patterns sometimes closer to those of the water and sometimes closer to those of the foliage. There is, in this technique, a structural sense resembling the brushwork of Cézanne at the same period. The predominant hues scattered in the painting are the gold of sunlight, the blue of the sky, and the green of the foliage. Throughout the surface the artist allows the mahogany tone of the panel itself to appear through the paint. He has yet to introduce the delicate violets of his mature style.

The purpose of these small sketches seems to have been the analysis of light in nature. But gradually from these studies the sense of a final composition would emerge in the artist's consciousness. For this final composition he would make drawing studies in charcoal of individual figures to add to the landscape. Finally, all would be orchestrated in a *magnum opus* in which form and color would play an equal part. The final painting would be as much a formal thesis on the art of painting as it would be a work of art. In the *Bathers* and the *Grand Jatte,* ordinary people stand and sit solemnly, obviously pawns in an elaborate compositional play, while their forms vibrate with small bits of colored light. The authenticity of the light effect surpasses even that of a Monet, conveying forcefully the full feeling of a warm, sunny afternoon. However, at each phase of Seurat's career, it is always the same light—the light of an ideal day, with no sense of change, no indication of weather. Reacting against the Impressionists, the Post-Impressionists sought a vision of permanence based upon universal truths about the world and about art.

1. Henri Dorra and John Rewald, *Seurat,* Paris, 1959, no. 98. (The Hyde painting is not included in this very complete study.)
2. *Ibid.,* p. 88.

Provenance: No. 103 of the inventory made at Seurat's death, of works remaining in his studio, by Félix Fénéon, Paul Signac, and Maximilien Luce; Jacques Dubourg, c. 1939; M. Bruneau; Watson Art Galleries, Montreal, 1947; purchased from Mortimer Brandt Gallery, New York, 1947.

Literature: C. M. de Hauke, *Seurat et son oeuvre,* Paris, 1961, p. 38, no. 67. Dated by De Hauke 1883, he erroneously described the work as "oil on canvas."

83. Paul Cézanne

French, 1839-1906

Trees, c. 1885. Verso, a portrait of Madame Cézanne in profile and a bathers group.

Watercolor over pencil on recto, pencil on verso. 19.5 x 11.8 cm. (7-11/16 x 4-5/8″) 1971.62
Inscribed in pencil lower left: "XXXVIII."

This unpublished watercolor was once page thirty-eight of a small sketchbook by Cézanne that has, at least until recently, been in the possession of the Cézanne expert Adrien Chappuis. At least twenty-five pages are missing from those numbered consecutively from I to LII. A pinhole in the upper right of the reverse side of the Hyde drawing suggests that the artist at one time pinned it to a wall or board so that the portrait of Madame Cézanne or the bathers group could be studied. A fully developed portrait of Madame Cézanne in precisely the same pose occurs on page forty-eight of the same notebook.[1]

The watercolor of trees is a characteristic example of Cézanne's intense analysis of his own visual responses to an out-of-door scene.

In the close-up portrait of Madame Cézanne, the nature of the object prevails over the artist's subjective response. Why Cézanne may have left the head incomplete and then redrew it on page forty-eight, could be due to the fact that the top of the head and ear are brought in too close to the edge of the profile to allow for the full sense of mass which the head required. In the final version these insufficiencies were corrected.

The bathers group is an example of Cézanne's life-long involvement with the theme of nude figures in a landscape. Beginning in the mythological subject of Diana and Actaeon, the subject of nude women bathing in a forest had, by the eighteenth century, become merely a decorative theme with conscious erotic overtones, shorn of any subject content. In the second half of the nineteenth century it was revived again as a major subject of French art, occurring in the work of such different artists as Courbet the Realist, Bouguereau the leading academic painter, and Renoir, friend of Cézanne and one of the Impressionists.

It seems clear that Cézanne was first attracted by the erotic nature of the bather subject. Later, it became his primary subject for experiments in composition. It appears that he hoped to transfer the aesthetic principles learned from his direct experience of landscape and still life, to an art form derived purely from the imagination. Models were not used for his bathers. Most of his studies of the nude human form were derived from works of art by other artists. For example, many of the drawings in the notebook from which the Hyde page was torn are of statues in the Louvre.

Chappuis dated this notebook 1884-87. Generally the bather subjects of a very similar arrangement are dated 1883-86. In 1885 this type of tree composition of large curves and diagonals first appears (e.g., *Village derrière les arbres,* c. 1885, Kunsthalle, Bremen).[2]

Thus, while it has been generally considered possible that Cézanne used his notebooks over extended periods of time, the painting and drawings on the Hyde page appear to be not far apart in date.

1. Listed as Chappuis 1 in Lionello Venturi, *Cézanne,* Paul Rosenberg, ed., Paris, 1936, pp. 304-306; Venturi lists the pages of this notebook following the Roman numeral pagination. Also see Chappuis, Adrien, *The Drawings of Paul Cézanne,* Greenwich, Conn., 1973, no. 665, etc.
2. Venturi, *op. cit.,* p. 159, no. 438.

Provenance: Paul Cézanne, the artist's son ?, Paul Guillaume ?; purchased from the Lilienfeld Galleries, New York, 1947.

84. Vincent van Gogh

Dutch, 1853-1890

Corner of a Field, 1888

Reed pen and brown ink over pencil on buff colored paper. 53.3 x 39.1 cm. (21 x 15-3/8″) 1971.81

The drawing depicts the corner of a field of grass which includes scattered fruit trees bare of leaves or blossoms. In the foreground some flowers are quickly sketched; in the background appears the distinctive tower of the ancient Romanesque Church of St. Trophîme, Arles. Thus one can precisely locate this drawing both in space and in time. The place is Arles, in Provence, in Southeastern France; the time is April 1888, before leaves or blossoms had appeared on the fruit trees. This is the month when the improving weather first made it possible for van Gogh to work out-of-doors during his stay in Arles. The drawing comes at the threshold of his great series of orchard paintings done later in April and during the month of May. The same towers, field, and trees occur in many paintings and drawings of this time.[1]

That a reed pen was used by the artist is both suggested by the technique and by a passage in a letter written to his brother Theo on April 20, 1888. "I sent the two drawings. These drawings were made with a reed sharpened the way you would a goose-quill; I intend to make a series of them."[2] In the stiff straight strokes required by the medium, van Gogh duplicated the visual energy of his brushwork when painting in oil. With the rapid ink loss that occurs with a reed pen, he was able to effect subtle gradations of tone in the rendering of the grass.

During this time in the development of his art, van Gogh's letters constantly allude to the art of Japan. The fruit trees and flowers, subjects of van Gogh's stay in Arles, are common to Japanese art. The fruit tree in the left hand corner of the Hyde drawing was rendered in what appears to be a Japanese manner, with stiff angular strokes, while the vibrant grass of the field resembles the grass depicted in the colored woodcut prints of the great Japanese landscape artist Hiroshige.

Van Gogh's art portrays his emotional reactions to his subjects. It became his artistic motive to energize the picture surface with shapes, brushwork, and colors in such a way as to provoke in the viewer an emotional response comparable to his own. In this emphasis upon experience over objective fact, the art of van Gogh reaches into the past, to Impressionism; that this experience is emotional looks forward to the future, to the style of twentieth century Expressionism.

1. J. B. de la Faille, *L'Oeuvre de Vincent van Gogh,* Paris and Brussels, 1928, nos. 409, 515, 516, 552, 600, etc.
2. Vincent van Gogh, *The Complete Letters of Vincent van Gogh,* Greenwich, Conn., 1958, p. 549.

Provenance: Madame Jo van Gogh Bonger; Sir Michael Ernest Sadler; Mrs. Cornelius J. Sullivan; purchased from the Parke-Bernet Galleries, Inc., 1939.

Literature: Exposition Musée Municipal, Amsterdam, 1905, no. 365; Ambroise Vollard, *Lettres de Vincent van Gogh à Émile Bernard,* 1911, pl. LXIII; Rotterdamsche Kunstkring, Rotterdam, van Gogh exhibit, March, 1923, no. 65; The Leicester Galleries, London, December 1923, no. 10; J. B. de la Faille, *L'Oeuvre de Vincent van Gogh,* Paris and Brussels, 1928, III, p. 153, no. 1516 and IV, pl. CLXXIV; Museum of Modern Art, New York, *Vincent van Gogh Exhibition,* 1935, no. 117; Parke-Bernet Galleries, Inc., New York, *Paintings, Drawings, Sculpture, Prints by Modern Artists, the Entire Collection of Mrs. Cornelius J. Sullivan,* December 6-7, 1939, no. 157, p. 64, illustrated; Munson-Williams-Proctor Institute, Utica, *Masters of Landscape East and West,* September 14-October 13, 1963, p. 61, illustrated; S. Lane Faison, Jr., *Art Tours and Detours in New York State,* New York, 1964, p. 117, fig. 197.

Exhibitions: Exposition Musée Municipal, Amsterdam, 1905; Rotterdamasche Kunsthkring, 1923; Leicester Galleries, London, 1923; Voor der Kunst, Utrecht, February-March, 1923; Museum of Modern Art, New York, 1935; The Minneapolis Institute of Arts (label on frame); Munson-Williams-Proctor Institute, Utica, September 14-October 13, 1963; Memorial Art Gallery, Rochester, November 1-December 1, 1963.

85. Pablo Picasso

Spanish/French, 1881-1973

Boy Holding a Blue Vase, c. 1905

Oil on canvas. 65.1 x 38.2 cm. (25-5/8 x 11-1/8″) 1971.34
Signed lower right: "Picasso."

The *Boy Holding a Blue Vase* is one of the last paintings of Picasso's Rose Period. It was executed late in 1905 at the threshold of the first of the series of artistic revolutions that were to punctuate his career. He had just seen the Fauves exhibition at the Salon d'Automne (Paris) where he encountered, in the paintings of Matisse and Rouault, an art stronger and more radical than his own. At about the same time he may have met Matisse (whose art was the one influence he would admit). The subjects of his Blue Period paintings are moody, while in the Rose Period they are sentimental. In the rather superficial smirk on the boy's face in the Hyde painting, Picasso may be in the process of eliminating human expression as an artistic effect in his painting style. His human forms in 1906 cease for a time to be emotive entities and become inert objects. In 1907 he carried this process to radical extremes in his *Woman of Avignon* (Museum of Modern Art, New York), where the human form is distorted more than ever before in Western art.

Near the end of 1905, Picasso executed a series of paintings of young men very similar to the Hyde *Boy Holding a Blue Vase.* The closest is the *Boy with a Bouquet* (collection of Mrs. John Winterstein, Villanova). Here the boy actually smiles, not strangely, but inanely. The *Blue Boy* (Warburg Collection, New York) is the same model, but in this instance the expression is serious.

The art of this phase of Picasso's career could be called post Post-Impressionist in style. Like the art of the Post-Impressionist Toulouse-Lautrec, it has an intriguing subject matter. At the same time Picasso pressed further the trend toward formal abstraction present in the work of the Post-Impressionists. While the *Boy Holding a Blue Vase* has an undistorted shape, the form is both too drastically simple and too flat to be in any way objectively real. A common paint texture unifies the picture surface artistically while it denies the distinguishing characteristics of flesh, cloth, and background.

The distant inspiration for these 1905 paintings of young men were possibly the *kouroi* statues of straight-standing, smiling young men of the Archaic period of early Greek sculpture. The costume still seems to be the simple tights worn by the tumblers of his Rose Period, but it is also a costume as unsuggestive of time or place as the nakedness of the *kouroi*. The pot the young man holds may suggest something Greek, since its shape is common among the pottery of ancient Greece. A single prop seems to have been essential to Picasso in the portraits of this time—a fan, a pipe, a bouquet—but it is unlikely that they are there to suggest a meaning. Picasso did not like to have his paintings interpreted. Rather, he wanted us to respond to them as to poetry, savoring their subtle moods.

Provenance: In 1943 Mrs. Hyde purchased the painting from Jacques Seligmann and Co., Inc., who gave Ambroise Vollard, the art dealer, as the only source. In 1906 Vollard gave Picasso 2,000 francs for more than thirty paintings, almost everything in his studio. It is likely that this painting was in that group. According to Daix and Bourdaille (see Literature) the *Boy Holding a Blue Vase* was in the collection of Picasso's friend, the sculptor Paco Durio, in 1905, and in a Flechtheim Collection, Düsseldorf, in 1912.

Literature: Christian Zervos, *Pablo Picasso,* Paris, c. 1942-1957, I, p. 120, no. 272, illustrated; George Boudaille and Pierre Daix, *Picasso; The Blue and Rose Periods,* Greenwich, Conn., n.d., (French ed. 1966), XIII, p. 279, no. 17, illustrated; Denys Sutton and Paolo Lecaldano, *The Complete Paintings of Picasso; Blue and Rose Periods,* New York, 1968, p. 104, 105, no. 215, illustrated p. 104.

86. Pablo Picasso

Spanish/French, 1881-1973

Four Figures, 1926

Pen and ink on paper. 29.2 x 38.1 cm. (11-1/2 x 15") 1971.76
Signed and dated lower left: "Picasso 26."

Four figures stand upon what appears to be a beach, that surreal shore which provides the setting for so many of Picasso's figure subjects. The male figure on the left is differentiated from the others; he is larger in scale and the viewer sees him from behind. His costume is ill-defined, though the short skirt may be vaguely Greek. He seems to contemplate the others in a way reminiscent of Picasso's print subjects of the artist contemplating his work. This is one of the common themes of his graphic work in this period. The artist figure places his hand on the shoulder of the next figure in line, and since they both face the same way, the viewer senses a relationship between the two. This second figure, with his long flowing hair and beard, can be recognized with certainty as a Greek philosopher type, a theme in art that originated in ancient Greece, flourished in Rome, and was revived in the Renaissance. (A famous example is the figure of Plato in Raphael's *School of Athens,* the Vatican, Rome.)

The female and male figures on the right are related to each other by their smaller scale, and by the fact that the woman rests her hand on the man's shoulder in a way somewhat resembling the manner in which the artist places his hand on the shoulder of the Greek philosopher. Like her companion, she wears a Spanish costume of the early nineteenth century. She rests her weight on a cane as if she, like the man beside her, were recovering from a wound. The costume of the male figure with bandaged head is that of a Spaniard at the time of the Napoleonic wars. The loose blouse and breeches, the short jacket, and the slipper-like shoes are the common dress of the male figures in Goya's series of etchings, *The Disasters of War.*

These figure types have no counterpart in any of Picasso's other work, implying that he perhaps had here a specific meaning in mind. Such imagery in a general sense goes back to his Rose Period, when he first developed the subject of picturesque human types standing quietly but provocatively in a barren landscape. Picasso's delicate linear style also stems from this early period.

There is in this drawing something of the idea of the artist contemplating his subject, and one may speculate about the artist's alliance with the philosopher on the one hand, and his direct interest in the real world on the other. However, Picasso usually made a point not to convey specific ideas with his works. Rather, like the Surrealists of the period, he provoked a rich array of feelings from the spectator through a dream-like juxtaposition of subjects, in this case, people, real in themselves, but improbable in their relationships.

While Picasso's graphic work of the 1920's continued in the Classic vein that seems to have been an unbroken undercurrent of his art, his paintings of the time still belong with Synthetic Cubism. Primarily they were still lifes done in a simplified, decorative Cubist manner.

Picasso's draftsmanship of the 1920's is usually more fluid than this, with the line often interrupted. While some of that fluidity is visible in the handling here, the line is still relatively straight-forward and is never interrupted. Thus the technique, like the subject matter, places this drawing in a peculiar and unique position relative to the rest of Picasso's work.

Provenance: Purchased from Jacques Seligmann and Co., Inc., New York, 1944.

Literature: Amadée Ozenfant, *Foundations of Modern Art,* New York, 1931, John Rodker trans., illustrated, p. 98.

Exhibitions: Drawings by Picasso, The Union Gallery of Union College at the Schenectady Museum, October 20-October 29, 1978.

87. Henri Matisse

French, 1869-1954

Two Draped Nudes, 1919. Verso, Three studies of a woman from the waist up,
seated upright, and sleeping on her folded arms.

Pencil on paper on recto, pen and ink on verso; watermark: "MBM."
28.1 x 38.4 cm. (11-1/16 x 15-1/8") 1971.74.2
Signed on recto lower left: "Henri Matisse."

This work and The Hyde Collection *Seated Nude* by Matisse (number 88) must belong to the same series of drawings. In both cases the figures are posed on a bed and the hair styles appear to be the same. The sheets of paper of both drawings are the same size, and both were manufactured by the Arches paper company. The distinctions in style between the two works may be accounted for by the fact that the subject of this entry would have been a preliminary study, while the *Seated Nude* would have been the final, more finished version. The fact that two poses of the same model are simultaneously seen would be more characteristic of a study. At the same time, the rendering is more tentative and less emphatic. In this, the earlier work, the artist is more concerned with the form he sees before him; in the later *Seated Nude* the artist's personal style comes more to the fore. The form in the later drawing is more flattened out, as in the artist's painting style, and shapes acquire a vividness which is absent from the earlier work. Studies in pen and ink on the verso of this sheet also imply a more casual use. They do not appear to be of the same model, nor is the style exactly the same. They probably were executed at a different time.

On a Kleeman Galleries label on the verso of *Two Draped Nudes,* a pencil inscription reads "ab. 1919." The drawing style seems characteristic of Matisse's at this date, and the model in both this work and in the *Seated Nude* resemble the model painted by Matisse at Nice during the winter of 1919. In the later *Seated Nude* the pose of the figure is related to the pose in a painting of this model (fully clothed) entitled *The Black Table* (Hahnloser Collection, Winterthur).

Provenance: It seems reasonably certain that this drawing came from the same source as the *Seated Nude;* the Kleeman Galleries, New York. A Kleeman Galleries label was on the back. On this label someone once wrote "2nd dealer." The first dealer was probably Scott and Fowles, New York, since two of their labels were once on the back. On one of these are the words, "from G. Jacquart, Paris."

185

88. Henri Matisse

French, 1869-1954

Seated Nude, 1919

Pencil on paper; watermark: "ARCHES." 38.4 x 28.3 cm. (15-1/8 x 11-1/8") 1971.74.1
Signed lower right: "Henri Matisse."

This drawing and the preceding *Two Draped Nudes* (number 87), may well have been executed at the same time. The watermarks probably came from two different sheets of the same pad. Both are the same size. In both the models are seated on beds and wear their hair in a similar fashion. It is probable that the present drawing was done later than the *Two Draped Nudes* because it is less a sketch and more a finished work of art. The pose of the single figure appears to be a further evolution of the two poses of the other drawing. This pose closely resembles that of the seated model in Matisse's painting, *The Black Table,* executed at Nice early in 1919 (Hahnloser Collection, Winterthur). There is also a similarity in facial type and hair styling. An early label on the back of the Hyde drawing dates it "about 1919" making a relationship between the two works probable, thus it is likely that both Hyde drawings were done in Nice in that year.

Most of Matisse's drawings concentrate on large, single human figures. Many seem not to have been studies for paintings but rather as ends in themselves. These drawings are distinguished from the paintings by the importance of the human form. In Matisse's paintings the human form is normally only one part of a larger compositional pattern.

In his handling of the nude Matisse allowed little personality to appear in the face or pose. Instead, he presented the form as an aggregation of strong shapes with the outline powerfully emphasized. A substantial mass is implied, if not described, through dense modeling. It is this primary interest in form over content that makes the work modern.

Provenance: Purchased from the Kleeman Galleries, New York (n.d.).

89. Charles Despiau

French, 1874-1946

Mask of Madame Despiau ?

Terra cotta. 21.6 x 12.7 x 7 cm. (8-1/2 x 5 x 2-3/4") 1971.94

Most of Despiau's art consists of sculptured portrait busts of his friends in terra cotta, marble, bronze, and plaster. Occasionally he executed a female nude. There seems to be no documents identifying this portrait with the artist's wife, although the title of the work goes back many years.

Despiau's style falls into a place in art history similar to that of Henri Matisse. Recognizable forms are retained while the artist feels sufficiently free from naturalistic requirements to push these forms firmly in an expressive direction. The mask-like shape of this study and the consciously flat treatment suggest the influence of primitive art.

Charles Despiau was born in Mont-de-Marsan, France. In 1891 he went to Paris to study sculpture. At the École des Arts Decoratif for two years, he was a student of Hector Lemaire, who had himself studied with Jean-Baptiste Carpeaux. For an additional three years he studied at the École des Beaux Arts in the atelier of Louis Barrias. Despiau first exhibited at the Salon of 1898. The most important art historical occurrence in his career happened in 1907 when Rodin asked him to join his studio, where Despiau worked for seven years. Despiau's first exhibition in the United States was at the Brummer Gallery, New York, in 1927.[1]

1. Research by Eleanor M. Hight.

Provenance: Purchased from the Brummer Gallery, Inc., New York, 1939.

90. Albert Bierstadt

German/American, 1830-1902

Yosemite Valley, c. 1865

Oil on canvas. 55.2 x 76.2 cm. (21-3/4 x 30") 1976.1
Signed lower left: "A Bierstadt."   Gift of Mr. and Mrs. Franklin Renz.

The view is of the portal to Yosemite Valley, with the cliffs of El Capitan on the left, and, on the right the Cathedral Rocks with Bridal Veil Falls, falling nine hundred feet to the valley below. In the foreground is the broad expanse of the Merced River.

Bierstadt camped at Yosemite for a number of weeks in August and September of 1863, where he did countless small sketches in oil on cardboard. Larger paintings were formed from these sketches after his return to New York City, the first being executed in 1864. His companion on the Western trip, Fitz Hugh Ludlow, described how the artist would "sit upon a camp stool beneath a large blue umbrella, his color box on his knees, his brush and palette in hand, and a clean board pinned in the cover of his color box."[1]

Almost the same composition as the Hyde painting appears in a much larger version in the Pioneer Museum and Haggin Galleries, Stockton, California. Even a fore-ground deer, a favorite motif of Bierstadt's, stands in the same position. In the larger painting, however, more of the scene is visible to the left and the right, including the full height of El Capitan.

In the Hyde painting, the cool light is that of morning. The western side of El Capitan is still in shadow, though the sun is sufficiently high to illuminate its southern face.

In his art Bierstadt continued the tradition of seeking the sublime in nature; that is, of depicting grand views where the power of nature is magnified. Here the sublime is subdued by a peaceful morning light and relaxed weather. The undisturbed deer in the foreground is to indicate the absence of man. Even at this early date a human presence might have been considered a contamination since nature had by this time replaced man in Anglo-American thought as the ideal of perfection and as the embodiment of the divine.

1. Fitz Hugh Ludlow, *Heart of the Continent,* New York, 1870, p. 9.

Provenance: The painting was acquired sometime in the 1940's by Mary Hyde Whitney.

91. Thomas Eakins

American, 1844-1916

In the Studio —Girl and Dog, c. 1884

Oil on canvas. 55.2 x 45.8 cm. (22-1/8 x 18-1/16″) 1971.17
Inscribed on back of canvas: "T.E."

An early label gives the title of this work as *In the Studio —Girl and Dog.* The girl cannot be identified, however Lloyd Goodrich may have been following a suggestion of Mrs. Eakins when he identified her as a student from one of Eakins' classes at the Pennsylvania Academy of Fine Arts. The setter dog which belonged to the artist was his constant companion during the 1880's and appears in a number of his paintings of the period.

In the Metropolitan Museum of Art, New York is a painting of Eakins' wife Sarah which shows a similar arrangement. This rendering was done in 1885, the following year. Eakins was married in 1884, the year the painting purportedly was done. It may be that the model of *In the Studio* served the artist as a lay figure in this first study for what was to be a portrait of Mrs. Eakins.

To facilitate its transfer to a larger canvas, the composition of this painting was laid out on a linear grid. This grid is still visible through the paint in a number of places. An almost exact replica of the upper half of the Hyde work is repeated in a watercolor (Philadelphia Museum of Art).

The broad brushwork of the Hyde painting indicates that it was a preparatory study for a larger work. It was characteristic of Eakins not to do preliminary drawings, but rather to make his initial studies in quickly painted oil sketches. He felt, as did the Romantic painters, that it was of great importance to capture the first impression of a subject. Thus, this painting would be the first step in a two-step process. The final painting, had it been executed, would probably have emphasized the pathetic feeling engendered by this plain face. Expressively the work would have belonged to a series of similar "pathetic" portrayals of women done by Eakins at this time, such as the 1881 *Pathetic Song* (Corcoran Gallery of Art, Washington, D.C.).

According to Lloyd Goodrich and Gordon Hendricks, this painting is supposed to have been signed with initials and dated on the lower right: "T.E. 1884."[1] However no inscription appears on the canvas. Hendricks observes that the signature was not by Eakins himself, therefore it may have been removed in conservation done at some time subsequent to Goodrich's inspection of the painting.

1. Lloyd Goodrich, *Thomas Eakins, His Life and Work,* New York, 1933, p. 178, no. 208; Gordon Hendricks, *The Life and Work of Thomas Eakins,* New York, 1974, p. 332, no. 166.

Provenance: Listed in the possession of Mrs. Eakins by Lloyd Goodrich in 1933. Indicated that purchase was made prior to 1937 when it was loaned to The Detroit Institute of Arts. Label on back of painting indicates it was from E. C. Babcock Gallery, New York.

Literature: Goodrich, *op. cit.,* p. 178; Roland McKinney, *Thomas Eakins,* New York, 1942, p. 99, illustrated; Carnegie Institute, *Thomas Eakins Centennial Exhibition, 1884-1944,* Pittsburgh, 1945, no. 93; Helen Foresman Spencer Museum of Art, University of Kansas; *Images: Twenty-three Interpretations,* April 26-June 3, 1964; S. Lane Faison Jr., *Art Tours and Detours in New York State,* New York, 1964, pp. 116-117, fig. 196; Hendricks, *op. cit.,* p. 332, illustrated.

Exhibitions: Pennsylvania Academy of Fine Arts (n.d.); Cleveland Museum of Art, 1927; Carnegie Institute, Pittsburgh, 1945; Helen Foresman Spencer Museum of Art, University of Kansas, April 26-June 3, 1964.

92. Thomas Eakins

American, 1844-1916

Portrait of Henry O. Tanner, 1902

Oil on canvas. 60.19 x 51.4 cm. (24-1/16 x 20-1/4") 1971.16
Signed lower right: "Eakins."

Henry O. Tanner, one of America's most important Black painters, was a student of Eakins at the Pennsylvania Academy of the Fine Arts from 1880 to 1882. He made his career in France, where he achieved a great success. In 1923 he was elected a Chevalier of the Legion of Honor. When Eakins executed this portrait of his former student in 1902, it is interesting to note that Tanner would have been the more acclaimed artist. In 1902 Tanner had returned to the United States for a brief visit. The date given for the painting by Goodrich and Hendricks, 1900, must be incorrect, since Tanner was not in this country at the time.[1]

The format and size of this portrait, a head and shoulders view facing to the left, place it in a category of similar works by Eakins in which the sitter usually is male, and was a personal friend or relative of the artist. His commissioned portraits are usually on a larger scale and include more than a head and shoulders. The portrait remained in Eakins' possession until his death. As was the case with all the contents of his studio, it was inherited by his wife Katherine.

1. Lloyd Goodrich, *Thomas Eakins, His Life and Work,* New York, 1933, p. 192, no. 345; Gordon Hendricks, *The Life and Work of Thomas Eakins,* New York, 1974, p. 332, no. 167.

Provenance: Mrs. Thomas Eakins; Babcock Galleries, New York ?; purchased in the 1930's.

Literature: San Francisco, Panama-Pacific Exposition, *Catalogue Deluxe of the Department of Fine Arts,* John E. D. Trask and J. Nelson Laurvik ed., San Francisco, 1915, II, p. 310, no. 2965; Pennsylvania Academy of the Fine Arts, *Memorial Exhibition of the Works of the Late Thomas Eakins,* Philadelphia, 1917, p. 86, no. 37; Alan Burroughs, "Thomas Eakins, the Man," *The Arts,* IV, no. 6, December 1923, pp. 302-323; Lloyd Goodrich, *op. cit.;* The Detroit Institute of Arts, *The Eighteenth Exhibition of American Art,* Detroit, 1937, p. 9, no. 17; Alain Locke, *The Negro in Art,* Washington, D.C., 1940, p. 164, illustrated; Howard University, *The Negro in the American Scene,* Washington, D.C., 1942, p. (5), illustrated; The Philadelphia Art Alliance, *Memorial Exhibition of Paintings by Henry O. Tanner,* Philadelphia, 1945, no. 19; Bowdoin College Museum of Art, *The Portrayal of the Negro in American Painting, 1710-1963,* Brunswick, Me., 1964, no. 56, illustrated; Sidney Kaplan, "The Negro in the Art of Homer and Eakins," *The Massachusetts Review,* VII, Winter 1966, p. 120, illustrated p. 119; Sylvan Schendler, *Eakins,* Boston, 1967, p. 290, fig. 137; Marcia M. Mathews, *Henry Ossawa Tanner, American Artist,* Chicago, 1969, p. 30; National Collection of Fine Arts, Smithsonian Institution, *The Art of Henry O. Tanner,* Washington, D.C., 1969, p. 46, no. 81, illustrated in frontispiece; Hale Woodruff, "My Meeting with Henry O. Tanner," *The Crisis,* LXXVII, January 1970, p. 7, illustrated; The Hyde Collection, *The Art of Henry Ossawa Tanner, 1859-1937,* Glens Falls, 1972, p. 14, no. 1, illustrated p. 3 and p. 14; Elsa Honig Fine, *The Afro-American Artist,* New York, 1973, p. 68, fig. 100; Gordon Hendricks, *op. cit.,* pp. 245, 248 and 332, no. 167, illustrated; Ellwood C. Parry, *The Image of the Indian and the Black Man in American Art, 1590-1900,* New York, 1974, pp. 163-168, fig. 116; Henry B. Rule, "Walt Whitman and Thomas Eakins Variations on Some Common Themes," *The Texas Quarterly,* XVII, Winter, 1974, p. 42, illustrated p. 44; San Jose Museum of Art, *Americans Abroad, Painters of the Victorian Era,* San Jose, Calif., December 1975-January 1976, illustrated; Metropolitan Museum of Art, *Selections of 19th Century Afro-American Art,* Catalogue by Regina A. Perry, New York, June-August, 1976, p. 22; Whitney Museum of American Art, *Turn of the Century America; Paintings, Graphics, Photos, 1890-1910,* June 29-October 2, 1977, p. 38, no. 33, illustrated p. 44.

Exhibitions: San Francisco Panama-Pacific Exposition, 1915; Pennsylvania Academy of the Fine Arts, 1917; The Detroit Institute of Arts, April 2-May 3, 1937; Howard University, Washington, D.C., 1942; The Philadelphia Art Alliance, October 2-November 11, 1945; Bowdoin College Museum of Art, Summer, 1964; National Collection of Fine Arts, Smithsonian Institution, Washington, D.C. A travelling exhibition opening in Washington July 22, 1969; Cleveland Museum of Art; McNay Museum of Art, New Orleans; Carnegie Institute, Pittsburgh; Rose Art Museum, Brandeis University, Waltham, Mass., 1969; The Hyde Collection, Glens Falls, July 6-August 31, 1972; San Jose Museum of Art, Calif., December 1975-January 1976; Metropolitan Museum of Art, New York, June-August, 1976; Whitney Museum of American Art, New York, June 29-October 2, 1977.

93. Elihu Vedder

American, 1836-1923

Palo. Ruins of an Old Castle, 1874

Oil on cardboard, mounted on canvas. 17.8 x 29.2 cm. (7 x 11-1/2") 1971.55
Signed lower right: "PALO. Aug. 1874. V."
Inscribed and signed on back: "Palo. Aug. 1974—near Rome—Vedder."

Palo. Ruins of an Old Castle was executed on the Italian coast near Rome while Vedder was on a sketching tour with the painter Nino Costa, a prominent member of the group of Italian artists known as the Macchiaioli.

There are two very different aspects to Vedder's art. During the winter he executed the highly artificial allegorical subjects upon which his fame was based; then in summer he painted small, straight-forward views of the Italian countryside. During the 1870's Vedder was asso-ciated with the Macchiaioli, who were considered to be artistic radicals because they ignored the sentimental, religious, and genre subjects dominating Italian art of the period, instead painting landscapes in a broad and coloristic manner that had many affinities with the style of the French Impressionists. Though disapproved of in their own time, the Macchiaioli are now considered to be the most important painters of nineteenth century Italy.

Provenance: Purchased from Anita Vedder (in Rome ?), 1930.

Literature: Regina Soria, *Elihu Vedder, American Visionary Artist in Rome (1836-1923),* 1970, p. 308, no. 245; The Hyde Collection, *Elihu Vedder, (1836-1923),* 1975, p. 23, no. 22.

94. Elihu Vedder

American, 1836-1923

Girl Reading in XVth Century Costume, 1879

Oil on paper mounted on canvas. 29.2 x 13.9 cm. (11-1/2 x 5-1/2″) 1971.54
Signed lower right: "Vedder."

While he was in Rome, Vedder painted this same model at least three times, probably in 1879 because the same face appears in Vedder's *Head of a Girl* (Museum of Fine Arts, Boston), signed and dated "1879." In Regina Soria's catalogue of Vedder's work, parenthetical notes give the model's name as "Eugenia."[1] The full-sleeved blouse and jumper-like dress of the model seem more to belong to the Italian sixteenth century than to the fifteenth century of the title. A similar costume is worn by Caravaggio's *Sleeping Magdalen,* c. 1595 (Doria Gallery, Rome), which may be a distant prototype for this painting.

In the second half of the nineteenth century, the idealized woman became a major subject for artists in America and Europe. In these portrayals the model's exotic costume or her nudity are devices which remove her from the real world to that of an ideal realm. The same is true of the pure white dress worn by women in paintings produced in the ambience of Impressionism, such as the two Childe Hassams in The Hyde Collection (numbers 102-103). Abbott Thayer often portrayed his women in Italian Renaissance dress. His daughter Mary, in the portrait in The Hyde Collection (number 107) wears a green velvet Renaissance costume that appears in a number of his other works.

A young girl quietly reading is a standard theme in nineteenth century portrayals of ideal women. This is probably a late manifestation of the old iconographical tradition of portraying the Virgin Mary reading, as in Jan van Eyck's *Ghent Altarpiece* (St. Bavo, Ghent). Certainly the ideal women subjects of the nineteenth century express virginal connotations.

The Hyde painting, small in scale and executed on paper, is characteristic of an American artistic practice: to execute studies in oil on paper. Vedder, therefore, never sold this painting. After the artist's death, it was purchased in 1930 directly from his daughter Anita who was living in Rome at the time.

1. Regina Soria, *Elihu Vedder, American Visionary Artist in Rome (1836-1923),* 1970, p. 322, no. 346.

Provenance: Purchased from Anita Vedder, Rome, 1930.

Literature: Soria, *op. cit.,* p. 322, no. 344, illustrated no. 26; The Hyde Collection, *Elihu Vedder (1836-1923),* 1975, p. 24, no. 26; Regina Soria, Joshua C. Taylor, Jane Dillenberger and Richard Murray, *Perceptions and Evocations: The Art of Elihu Vedder,* Washington, 1979, p. 105, illustrated, no. 122.

Exhibitions: National Collection of Fine Arts, Smithsonian Institution, Washington, D.C., October 13, 1978-February 4, 1979; The Brooklyn Museum, New York, April 28-July 9, 1979.

95. Elihu Vedder

American, 1836-1923

Marriage of the Daughter of the Vine, c. 1890

Oil on canvas. 85.1 x 152.4 cm. (33-1/2 x 60″) 1971.296
Signed lower right: "Elihu Vedder."   Gift of Caroline L. Brown.

The painting illustrates a verse from the famous poem, the *Rubaiyat* by Omar Khayyam. At the time of the painting, Edward Fitzgerald's free translation of the poem was tremendously popular. It is his poetry, as much as Omar's, that appears in the following quatrain 59:

> You know my friends, with what a brave Carouse
> I made a Second Marriage in my house;
> Divorced old barren Reason from my Bed,
> And took the Daughter of the Vine to Spouse.

In 1884 Houghton, Mifflin and Company, Boston, published a *Rubaiyat* illustrated by Vedder which had great success both in the United States and in England. Although the Hyde painting has more details it follows closely his illustration for quatrain 59. A landscape view and draperies replace a blank wall, and the figures sit on a bench rather than on a ledge. A basin of flowers was added by the artist, and flowers replace the vine leaves which are worn by the women in the illustration. On the right in the painting the *bacchante* figure plays the double pipe that commonly appears in the bacchic scenes in Greek vase painting.

Vedder handles the allegorical arrangement in the *Marriage of the Daughter of the Vine* in a way common both in this country, and in the art of the Pre-Raphaelites in England. As in Botticelli's *Primavera* (Uffizi, Florence), the standard prototype for nineteenth century allegorical painting, female figures carry the burden of the meaning. These figures are partly derived from earlier sources and partly invented by the artist, but when invention occurs, it is usual for the title of the work to give a clear guide to the spectator's interpretation of it. Cold Reason on the right is pure fabrication on Vedder's part. She has an appropriately severe face and is dressed in the heavy, gray, concealing robes of a monk. In her left arm she carries books, while in her right hand is a set of calipers. An owl, representing wisdom, an ancient attribute of Athena, sits on her shoulder. The lamp beside her is somewhat more subtle. The light from the lamp refers to reason, while the sphinx ornament that holds the lamp reminds the viewer of the riddle of the sphinx, and by extension, of the mysteries of the universe which are resolved by reason.

The older man on the left is, of course, Omar himself, who casts out Reason with a clear-cut gesture. In his right hand he holds the cup of wine that he now prefers. The cup is saucer-like in the Greek manner and the marriage to the daughter of the vine is cast in Greek dress, with symbols of Dionysos/Bacchus, the Greek god of wine. Beside the daughter of the vine is the staff of Bacchus, the Thyrsus with a pine cone on top. The two other women are clearly bacchantes, those female followers of Bacchus who appear so often in Greek vase paintings, dancing, and playing tamborines and double pipes. A bacchic scene is actually illustrated on the wine jar, or amphora, which stands on the far left.

The flowers in the basin on the bench, in the hand of the *Daughter of the Vine* and which all the women wear in their hair, are references to marriage.

Vedder was born in New York City, and studied art in Paris and Florence from 1855-60. In the 1860's in Boston, he became friends with the painters William Morris Hunt and John LaFarge. In 1869 he was married in Glens Falls, New York, to Elizabeth Caroline Beach Rosekrans. From that time most of Vedder's artistic life was spent in Italy where he died in 1923. During his lifetime he was to become one of America's best known artists.

Provenance: Gift of Caroline L. Brown of Glens Falls, a direct descendant of the artist. The painting appears in a photograph of Vedder working in his studio, illustrated, p. 237 in Soria, see Literature.

Literature: Regina Soria, *Elihu Vedder, American Visionary Artist (1836-1923),* 1970, p. 338, no. 474; The Hyde Collection, *Elihu Vedder (1836-1923),* 1975, p. 24, no. 31, illustrated, p. 14; National Collection of Fine Arts, Smithsonian Institution, *The Art of Elihu Vedder,* Washington, D.C., 1979, no. 224; Regina Soria, Joshua C. Taylor, Jane Dillenberger and Richard Murray, *Perceptions and Evocations: The Art of Elihu Vedder,* Washington, D.C., 1979, p. 142-145, illustrated, no. 179.

Exhibitions: National Collection of Fine Arts, Smithsonian Institution, Washington, D.C., October 13, 1978-February 4, 1979; The Brooklyn Museum, New York, April 28-July 9, 1979.

96. John Frederick Peto

American, 1854-1907

Still Life with Mug, Pipe, and Book, 1880

Oil on cardboard. 20.3 x 25.4 cm. (8 x 10") 1971.33
Signed and dated on back: "John F. Peto 1880."

Painted often by Peto, the beer stein, pipe, and book in the Hyde still life probably were considered by the artist to be symbols of idleness. They would have represented a kind of leisure frowned upon in nineteenth century America, where business was the only proper masculine concern. Such a muted moralizing message was often carried by the still life painting of seventeenth century Holland, as is the case with The Hyde Collection's *Vanitas Still Life* by the painter Edwaert Colyer (number 54). It is interesting to note that a different kind of painting by Colyer may have influenced Peto's work. In 1706 Colyer painted a rack still life, where flat objects are attached to a board by ribbons. In 1878 Peto began the first of a long series of very similar still lifes, suggesting a direct knowledge of Colyer's work.

Dated 1880, this painting would be one of the earliest recorded for John F. Peto. It is important historically because it confirms the close relationship that must have existed between Peto and the painter of still lifes, William M. Harnett. An association between the two artists would have occurred between the years 1875-80, in Philadelphia. At this time the mug and pipe were the most common objects in Harnett's still lifes. Peto apparently collected still life objects that were close duplicates of those in Harnett's paintings, evidence of his life-long devotion to his fellow artist's work.[1] The mug is a German beer stein so similar to one Harnett owned it would be difficult to tell the two apart. The pipe is a meerschaum. In the Hyde painting Peto even imitated Harnett's peculiar technical experiment of the time, an attempt to duplicate by impasto the surface relief of the object.

Peto and Harnett were two of the most important painters of still life in nineteenth century America. In his own time Peto received very little recognition while Harnett acquired both fame and fortune. Consequently, many of Peto's paintings received forged Harnett signatures, even though their styles evolved along quite different paths. When, in 1939, Harnett's own name was brought from obscurity by an exhibit at the Downtown Gallery, New York City, many of the paintings ascribed to him were actually by Peto. Ten years later Peto's distinct style was defined by Alfred Frankenstein's article in the *Art Bulletin* of March, 1949.[2]

1. Alfred Frankenstein, *After the Hunt,* Los Angeles, 1969, p. 14.
2. _____ , "Harnett, True and False," *Art Bulletin,* XXXI, March, 1949, pp. 38-56.

Provenance: Purchased from M. Knoedler and Co., Inc., New York, 1955.

97. Winslow Homer

American, 1836-1910

Forebodings, 1881

Watercolor on paper. 36.8 x 52 cm. (14-1/2 x 21-1/2") 1971.69
Signed and dated lower left: "Winslow Homer 1881."

Dated 1881, this watercolor was executed while Homer was at Tynemouth, on the Northumberland coast in England. He had rented a small cottage in the tiny fishing village of Cullercoats nearby, where the Tyne River joins the sea. His principal subjects became the heroic fishermen's wives. The portrayal of men in their struggle against the sea came at a later time in his artistic development. Women had been the main theme of Homer's art in the preceding decade. At first they appear as young maidens, idyllically conceived among flowers, playing at games or, significantly, standing on the seashore. At Tynemouth the women are mature. Set against a somber and threatening sea, they stoically await the return of their husbands. These Tynemouth women are to be admired as heroines. Their forms are full-limbed and handsome; their facial types possibly had been modeled after Greek prototypes. This idealization of simple folk who live close to nature is an aspect of nineteenth century Romanticism, associated both with its devotion to nature and its social egalitarianism. At

Tynemouth Homer would have more often observed women, the men being away at sea. Hence the stoical theme of women waiting becomes the principal subject of his watercolors of the period. The image of the Hyde work, heroic women silhouetted against the sea, must have had special significance for Homer. It was repeated in major works at periodic intervals for the remainder of the artist's career.

In the Hyde painting the women are compacted into a monumental block, a veritable pillar of strength. We see in this compositional device how Homer's ability to express concepts and feelings in artistic form developed to full maturity during his visit to England. At the same time he acquired the range of subject matter that was to establish his fame as an artist. It was not long after his return to the United States in 1882, that Homer moved to Prout's Neck on the coast of Maine to spend the rest of his life in an environment comparable to the one he had found at Tynemouth.

Provenance: Thomas B. Clarke, 1891; M. Knoedler and Co., Inc.; purchased from E. and A. Milch, Inc., New York, before 1939.

Literature: Pennsylvania Academy of the Fine Arts, Philadelphia, Thomas B. Clarke Collection, Fall, 1891; William Howe Downes, *The Life and Works of Winslow Homer,* Boston and New York, 1911, pp. 100-103; Nathaniel Poussette-Dart, *Winslow Homer, Distinguished American Artists Series,* New York, 1923, p. (65), illustrated; Gordon Hendricks, *The Life and Work of Winslow Homer,* New York, 1979, p. 307, no. CL-398, illustrated.

Exhibitions: Pennsylvania Academy of the Fine Arts, Philadelphia, Fall, 1891; The Copley Society of Boston Exhibition of American Water Colors, Paris, 1923.

98. Winslow Homer

American, 1836-1910

A Good One, Adirondacks, 1889

Watercolor over a light pencil sketch on paper. 31.1 x 49.5 cm. (12-1/4 x 19-1/2") 1971.68
Signed and dated lower right, and lower left, in the same fashion: "Winslow Homer 1889."

An Adirondack guide in a rowboat dominates the painting. Typical of Homer's fishing subjects, the observer is brought into the scene at the exciting moment when a fish is about to be caught. At the same time we are conscious of the artist's larger purpose: to portray man in a close dialogue with nature. This nature he invariably universalizes by avoiding recognizable topographical references. While supposedly in the Adirondacks, this scene could be anywhere in the temperate zone. Philip C. Beam has observed that many of Homer's Adirondack watercolors were actually painted at his studio, Prout's Neck, Maine.[1]

Homer first visited the Adirondacks in 1870, drawn by the incomparable hunting and fishing.[2] At that time the Adirondacks were much as they are today, the largest wilderness in the Eastern United States. On his first visit Homer was a guest of the painter Russell M. Shurtleff in Keene Valley.[3] In 1889 he and his brother Charles joined a group who purchased a large tract of land south of the High Peaks region in the town of Minerva.[4] The North Woods Club, which they organized, still exists. It was in that same year that the Hyde watercolor was painted. At this same time there occurred a dramatic transformation in the artist's style. Colors brightened; pigment was laid on in broad, transparent pools. Generally his technique became more impressionistic in the manner of the French painter Monet. There is no evidence of a direct influence, although Homer must certainly have been aware of the French artist's achievement. The first major exhibition of French Impressionist painting had been held in New York three years before, in 1886. Still, French Impressionism would have only confirmed for Homer goals already set. He had used bright colors as early as 1884 during a trip to the Bahamas. His preference for the watercolor medium was the ease with which it could be managed out-of-doors. Like the Impressionists he sought an authentic effect of natural light by studying its effects at the scene, though it was common for Homer to complete his watercolors in his studio. Another value of watercolor for Homer must have been the fact that the brilliance of the paper could be made to act throughout the picture surface, approximating the brilliance of daylight. It could be made to shine through transparent washes; sparkle through the many small openings left by dragging a brush over rough paper; and, where the paper was fully exposed in untouched passages, or where the artist removed paint with a scraper, it could flash like the full glare of sunlight.

1. Philip C. Beam, *Winslow Homer at Prout's Neck,* Boston and Toronto, 1966, p. 99.
2. Lloyd Goodrich, *Winslow Homer,* New York, 1944, p. 57.
3. *Ibid.*
4. *Ibid.,* p. 114.

Provenance: Purchased by Winslow Homer's friend and patron William T. Evans, from Gustav Reichard, Homer's New York dealer, possibly from the large exhibition of Homer's Adirondack watercolors of 1889 held at Reichard's in 1890. Evans sale, American Art Galleries, 1913; M. Knoedler and Co., Inc.; Sam Lewisohn; William Macbeth, Inc.; purchased from William Macbeth, Inc., 1939.

Literature: *New York Times Book Review,* July 18, 1926, p. 16, illustrated under the caption "Pickerel or Pike?"; Forbes Watson, "American Collections No. III — The Adolph Lewisohn Collection," *The Arts,* July, 1926, illustrated p. 42; Gordon Hendricks, *The Life and Work of Winslow Homer,* New York, 1979, p. 307, no. CL-399, illustrated.

Exhibitions: Metropolitan Museum of Art, New York, 1951; State University of New York at Plattsburgh, New York, January 9-January 30, 1972.

99. Winslow Homer

American, 1836-1910

St. John's River, Florida, 1890

Watercolor on paper. 34.2 x 50.5 cm. (13-1/2 x 19-7/8″) 1971.70
Signed and dated lower right: "Homer 1890."

Since fishing was Homer's favorite sport, it is tempting to imagine that his many renderings of the subject were painted from the very boat from which he would cast his line. Surrounded with water, it is natural enough that watercolor would be his preferred medium. In a more general sense he preferred watercolor for subjects that were closer to life and less artistically serious. Large exhibition pieces with contrived subjects he executed in oil.

In February and March of 1890 Homer stayed at the Brock Hotel at Enterprise, south of Jacksonville, Florida on Lake Monroe, a wide place in St. John's River, famous for its bass fishing. His first fishing trip to Florida had been in 1886. He returned again during the winters of 1903-4 and 1904-5. During the 1890 visit Homer executed nine watercolors of the flat river bordered by its bands of trees. In three of these bass fishermen appear. The boat and fisherman in the present work were added after the painting was completed, being scraped into the surface. Scrapers were standard tools of the nineteenth century watercolor artist. Almost all of Homer's watercolors show some evidence of the use of these tools.

Homer's simple compositions, where nature appears as two or three broad bands of color, are characteristic of a general trend in landscape painting in America at this time. One sees such compositions in the later work of George Inness, and in the paintings of J. Francis Murphy, Alexander Wyant, Homer D. Martin, George Smillie, Henry Ward Ranger, and Robert Swain Gifford—enough artists to produce a school comparable in scope to the Hudson River School.

Provenance: Charles S. Homer, the artist's brother; Mrs. Charles S. Homer; Arthur P. and Charles L. Homer; purchased from William Macbeth, Inc., 1938.

Literature: University of Florida, Gainesville, Fl.; *Artists of the Florida Tropics,* 1965, no. 38; Cummer Gallery of Art, Jacksonville, *Winslow Homer's Florida, 1886-1909,* Jacksonville, 1977, p. 24, no. 16, illustrated; Gordon Hendricks, *The Life and Work of Winslow Homer,* New York, 1979, p. 307, no. CL-400, illustrated.

Exhibitions: The Brooklyn Museum, March 28, 1917 (from label); William Macbeth, Inc., *Paintings by American Artists* (1938?) (from label); University of Florida, Gainesville, March 1-31, 1965; Cummer Gallery of Art, April 22-May 29, 1977.

100. Frank Duveneck

American, 1848-1919

Munich Professor, c. 1879

Oil on canvas. 40.95 x 30.35 cm. (16-1/2 x 11-15/16") 1971.15
Signed in monogram lower left: "F D."

The portrait shows the height of Duveneck's Munich style, with spontaneous brushstrokes describing the form with a series of small facets or planes, and with the immediacy of the sitter, portrayed as in a portrait by Frans Hals, looking out and reacting to the spectator.[1]

The broad style suggests that the painting was executed during Duveneck's second visit to Munich in 1879—if the portrait is indeed of a Munich professor as the traditional title of the painting indicates. Duveneck was first in Munich in 1870 as a student at the Royal Academy. Two years later he was joined by another American painter William Merritt Chase. The two became close friends and later, through their art and teachings, they became leaders of what came to be called the Munich School of American painting. This Munich style, derived from the seventeenth century Dutch painting techniques of Rembrandt and Hals, was characterized by broad brushwork, a dark tonality, and colors which gravitated toward the reds, browns, and blacks.

Duveneck returned to the United States in 1874. For three years he was a protégé of the very successful painter William Morris Hunt, achieving a distinguished success in his own right in Boston and Cincinnati. In 1878 Duveneck returned to Munich to start his own school of painting. It was not until about that time that his style arrived at the full breadth of treatment evident in the Hyde work. After the artist went to Italy in 1880, he painted with brighter colors, thus the time of the Hyde painting could be limited to the years 1878-79.

1. Research and conclusions by Eleanor M. Hight.

101. Willard Leroy Metcalf

American, 1858-1925

Zuni Indians, 1883

Gouache on paper. 23.7 x 35.2 cm. (9-5/16 x 13-7/8″) 1971.104
Signed and dated lower left: "Metcalf Zuñi '83."

This work has all of the characteristics of a drawing prepared to be copied by a wood-engraver for a magazine illustration. In 1881 Metcalf traveled to New Mexico in the company of Sylvester Baxter, a writer for the *Boston Herald,* apparently to do a series of articles on the Zuni Pueblo Indians. The Zunis had just been brought to the attention of the world by the extraordinary work of the first anthropologist of the Smithsonian Institution, Frank H. Cushing. Like Cushing, Metcalf joined into the lives of the Zuni, to the point of being initiated into one of their secret orders. He was to remain in New Mexico for three years. Baxter's first article with Metcalf's illustrations appeared in *Harpers New Monthly Magazine* in June, 1882.[1] Later, in 1883, Metcalf was one of the illustrators of a three-part article written by Cushing himself for the *Century Magazine.*[2] The date, format, and style of the Hyde drawing suggest that it was prepared as an illustration for Cushing's articles, though it was never used.

It is certain that the time of execution would be the early months of 1883, since sometime in May Metcalf left New Mexico, traveling east across the United States and directly across the Atlantic to Europe. On July 5 he arrived in London. Later, in Paris, like so many American artists of his generation, he studied at the Academy Julien. Metcalf was in Paris for six years, coming gradually under the influence of such Impressionists as Monet. Metcalf's characteristic style after his return to America in 1890 was modified Impressionism. He painted simple, freshly colored landscapes, surprisingly devoid of human content, in contrast to his richly human early work among the Zunis.

1. Sylvester Baxter, "The Father of the Pueblos," *Harpers New Monthly Magazine,* LXV, June, 1882, p. 72ff.
2. Frank H. Cushing, "My Adventure in Zuni," *The Century Magazine,* November, 1882-April 1883, pp. 191 and 500 and May 1883-October, 1883, p. 28.

Literature: James K. Ballinger, *Beyond the Endless River,* Phoenix Art Museum, Ariz., 1979, pp. 158-159, pl. 75.

Exhibitions: Phoenix Art Museum, 1979; Fine Arts Gallery of San Diego, 1979; Wichita Art Museum, 1979.

102. Childe Hassam

American, 1859-1935

Geraniums, 1888

Oil on canvas. 46.3 x 32.9 cm. (18-1/4 x 12-15/16″) 1971.22
Signed and dated lower left: "Childe Hassam 1888."
Signed in monogram and dated on the back in red paint: "C H 1889" (after the addition of more flowers ?).

Childe Hassam is considered to be America's most important Impressionist painter, the artist whose style is closest to that of the great French Impressionist Monet. In 1888, when *Geraniums* was painted, he had yet to take the plunge into the full range of brilliant colors of the Impressionist technique. An old label on the back of the painting tells exactly where it was done, on the "porch of a French country house and garden at Villiers-le-Bel north of and near Paris." In fact, Villiers-le-Bel lies eleven miles straight north of the center of the city. The "French country house" belonged to a friend of Hassam's. It was where he and his wife Kathleen spent their summers. The girl in the painting who quietly reads must certainly be Kathleen.

They had been married in Boston, three years before in 1885. The following year they went to Paris, where Hassam rented an apartment on Montmartre and studied life drawing under the academic painters Boulanger and Lefebvre. But before this, Hassam's choice of subject matter had already been set in a direction quite different from that of the artificial costume dramas of the French academic manner. His *Boston Common at Twilight,* 1885 (Museum of Fine Arts, Boston), combines a direct realism of place with an atmospheric mood reminiscent of Whistler's already well-known style. Realism of place is what is also encountered in *Geraniums.* But as in his *Boston Common at Twilight,* it is a selected realism, where a gentle and idyllic mood is generated by the character of the subject. It is interesting and perhaps important to note that the figure of a quiet young woman, often faceless as here, but still with intimations that she would be attractive, became a standard prop in a certain kind of nineteenth century painting where the setting is more often than not a garden, or a close view of a landscape. The subject is one aspect of the general aesthetic idealization of women that occurred in art during the latter half of the century.

Provenance: Purchased from E. and A. Milch, Inc., May, 1930.

Literature: William H. Gerdts, *American Impressionism,* Henry Art Gallery, University of Washington, Seattle, 1980, p. 62, illustrated.

Exhibitions: A stamp on the back reads "1889/Salon," suggesting that the work was exhibited at the great Salon exhibit, Paris, in 1889; Henry Art Gallery, University of Washington, Seattle, January 3-March 2, 1980; Frederick S. Wight Gallery, University of California at Los Angeles, March 9-May 4, 1980; Terra Museum of American Art, Evanston, Illinois, May 16-June 22, 1980; Institute of Contemporary Art, Boston, July 1-August 31, 1980.

103. Childe Hassam

American, 1859-1935

Girl in Pink/In the Garden, 1896

Pastel on sandpaper. 76.5 x 61.6 cm. (30-1/8 x 24-1/4″) 1971.67
Signed and dated lower right: "Childe Hassam 1896."

In this pastel a young girl stands before a bush in brilliant sunlight. She wears a white dress, which reflects a red light, possibly from a nearby building, and blue from the sky. Using the quick medium of pastel, Hassam was able to record the fleeting colored light of the scene in a full Impressionist manner. In true Impressionism, as art history now defines it, the artist uses brilliant hues to imitate the color intensity of forms seen in outdoor light. At the same time he fills each form with the variety of hues that are naturally reflected throughout the visible world. The idea was to make the work of art a full equivalent of a true visual experience.

While Hassam was in France from 1886 to 1889, he associated with the circle of artists who surrounded the leader of the French Impressionists, Claude Monet. However, he did not adopt the Impressionist system of bright colors and broken brushwork until sometime after his return to America in 1895. By that time there had developed a strong market for French Impressionist painting in America, and it was apparently in response to this market that he adjusted his style.

Unlike the French Impressionists, Hassam depended upon interesting subject matter. In the present work the figure of the girl is as intriguing as are the effects of light. When the work was purchased, it was suggested by the art dealer Norman Hirschl that the girl portrayed was a member of the Temple family of Boston who had owned the pastel until its sale to the Gallery.

Provenance: Temple family, Boston; purchased from Hirschl and Adler Galleries, Inc., New York, 1959.

104. James Abbott McNeill Whistler ?

American, 1834-1903

Tatting, c. 1890

Oil on wooden panel. 29.7 x 22.1 cm. (11-3/4 x 8-3/4″) 1971.59

A girl in nineteenth century dress is seated on a diagonal bench. The traditional title of the work suggests she is tatting, though the breadth of the brushwork makes the activity of her hands unclear. A ball of yarn rolls to the floor. The direct and contemporary nature of the subject relates it to the genre themes of the French Impressionists.

This painting has always been attributed to James McNeill Whistler until the suggestion was made by the Whistler expert Andrew McLaren Young, that the style resembles more the painting of Whistler's wife, Beatrix.[1] Whistleresque in many of its particulars, the brushwork in the painting would place it in a category with a certain type of preliminary sketch Whistler would execute on panel in extremely broad strokes. According to Andrew McLaren Young, a number of paintings in a similar style attributed to Whistler are actually by Beatrix, but the problem of separating the hands of the two artists has still to be solved.

Whether by Whistler himself, his wife, or by a third artist in Whistler's ambience, the Hyde painting is striking for its quality and its originality. Radical is the way the image of the girl tatting is the vehicle for an extraordinary activity of brushwork. Freed from any representational function, the paint lies flat on the picture surface, counteracting illusions of space. One can imagine such a work as by the hand of one of Whistler's younger disciples, carrying further the master's ideas along a path that led ultimately to abstract art.

1. Direct verbal communication during a visit to The Hyde Collection.

Literature: S. Lane Faison, Jr., *Art Tours and Detours in New York State,* New York, 1964, p. 116, fig. 195.

105. James Abbott McNeill Whistler

American, 1834-1903

The Sea, Pourville, No. 1, 1899

Oil on wooden panel. 17.8 x 25.9 cm. (7 x 10-3/4") 1971.58
Signed lower right with butterfly.

The original title of this work, probably given to it by Whistler himself, appears in the Anderson Gallery sale catalogue of February, 1920, lot no. 115, where *The Sea, Pourville No. 2* was also sold. (The latter, originally in the Albany Institute of History and Art, now belongs to the Munson-Williams-Proctor Institute, Utica.) It appears reasonably certain that the two paintings were executed in 1899, between July 22 and August 7, during Whistler's visit to Pourville, France, near Dieppe. He had rented a house for Miss Birnie Philip and her mother, where he stayed at periodic intervals.[1] The Pourville beach was Whistler's favorite location for doing seascapes. Always small and on panel, these paintings were executed at the scene in *plein air* after the fashion of the French Impressionists. Whistler once explained his way of painting the sea to his apprentice Mrs. Addams. "When the wave broke and the surf made a beautiful line of white, he painted this at once, then all that completed the beauty of the breaking wave, then the boat passing, and then, having got the movement and the beauty that goes almost as soon as it comes, he put in the shore or the horizon."[2] For all of Whistler's concern for abstract form in his style, it appears that he was closely bound to a direct experience of the scene.

The drastic simplicity of this work is both its most striking and its most significant aspect. Nature is reduced to three essential tonal bands of paint. It is the paint quality that dominates the picture, more than the characteristics of sea or sky. Perhaps more than any artist in the *avant-garde* movement in nineteenth century art, Whistler anticipated the philosophy and methods of modern painting. His art may be described as a reduction of natural forms to the point where separate characteristics are sacrificed to a close harmony of the picture surface. In dramatic contrast to the way the Impressionists sought to embrace all the colored lights of nature in their canvases, Whistler arrived at a virtual monochrome by banishing every kind of variation or contrast.

1. Andrew McLaren Young, Margaret MacDonald, and Robin Spencer, *The Paintings of James McNeill Whistler,* New Haven and London, 1980, p. 219.
2. Quoted in E. R. and J. Pennell, *The Life of James McNeill Whistler,* 6th ed., Philadelphia and London, 1919, p. 367.

Provenance: Originally in the collection of A. Arnold Hannay (Pennell; *The Life of James McNeill Whistler.* See Literature); sold to Mrs. Lewis Hind by art dealer Croal Thomson, 1919; Anderson Galleries, New York, February 5-6, 1920, lot 115; Anderson Galleries, April 14, 1926, lot 52; purchased from E. and A. Milch, Inc., November 21, 1929.

Literature: The International Society of Sculptors, Painters, and Gravers, London; *An Illustrated Catalogue of the Whistler Memorial Exhibition,* 1905, p. 101, no. 64, *The Sea at Pourville.* (The problem is that the dimensions are given as 4 x 6-1/2); E. R. and J. Pennell, *op. cit.,* p. 214, illustrated opposite p. 416; Andrew McLaren Young, letters in the Hyde Archives; Andrew McLaren Young, Margaret McDonald, and Robin Spencer, *op. cit.,* p. 219, no. 516; II, pl.330.

Exhibitions: London, 1905; Tate Gallery, London, 1912; The University of Michigan Museum of Art, Ann Arbor, August 27-October 8, 1978.

106. J.(ohn) Francis Murphy

American, 1853-1921

Landscape, c. 1894

Oil on canvas. 20.3 x 30.5 cm. (8 x 12″) 1971.30
Signed lower right with illegible date: "J. Francis Murphy '94" (?).

The view in this painting is of a simple, flat landscape. Devoid of distinct topographical features, it could be anywhere in the temperate zone, though it was most certainly painted in America.

Murphy, called the Corot of America for certain affinities that exist between his style and that of the great French master, was a well-known and greatly respected artist in this country in the late nineteenth century. His style may be classified with that of a whole group of American artists who belong to what could be designated a third generation of American landscape painting. Thomas Cole and Asher B. Durand would represent the first; Albert Bierstadt, Frederick Church, and John F. Kensett, the second. Two of the leading artists of the third generation were Murphy's close friends, George Inness and Alexander Wyant. Like Winslow Homer, Murphy was often a guest of the painter R. G. Shurtleff at Keene Valley, New York. Later he was associated with Homer D. Martin and John Twachtman. This third generation of landscape artists painted in a style distinguished by its great simplicity of form, by its close, intimate views, and by its rich paint textures. Influenced by the French Barbizon school, this style would almost appear to be a reaction against the vast panoramas, dramatic luminosity, and tight paint surfaces of earlier generations of American landscape art. Its values would be less obvious, more subtle and artistic.

J. Francis Murphy was born in Oswego, New York. After the age of twelve his formal education came to an end, but he must have already been educating himself in the field of art. When he was fifteen, his family moved to Chicago where he was able to make drawings of the great fire of 1871. In 1873 Murphy was in Saratoga Springs, New York. He opened a studio in New York City in 1875, but in the summer returned to Saratoga Springs to stay with his friend, the famous publisher Frank Leslie. In 1886 Murphy was in France where he was associated with an American colony of artists at Montigny.

After 1900 Murphy was influenced by Monet, but his reaction to Monet's style was peculiar. He would cover a canvas with Monet's bright colors and broad brushwork, but he then would treat it as underpainting, softening and blending this Monet-like surface with an overlay of darker glazes.[1]

Except for Winslow Homer this whole generation of landscape painters faded from view with the general downgrading of American landscape painting that occurred in the first half of the twentieth century. Today Cole, Bierstadt and Church have been revived. Of Murphy's generation Inness, Wyant, Martin, and Twachtmen have become generally known. But the extreme minimalism of Murphy's style is still both too radical and too subtle to have attracted the attention of a general art viewing public.

1. Complete information on the artist J. Francis Murphy, and a catalogue raisonné had been assembled in an unpublished manuscript by the late Dr. Emerson Kelly of Albany, New York. The present location is unknown.

107. Abbott Handerson Thayer

American, 1849-1921

Mary: Portrait of the Artist's Daughter, 1894 and/or 1902

Oil on canvas. 60.9 x 55.8 cm. (24 x 22") 1971.46
Signed lower right: "Abbott Thayer."

The earliest document that mentions the Hyde portrait of Abbott Thayer's daughter Mary is a letter to Thayer from his lifelong friend, the painter Thomas Dewing. The letter was sent a week before Thayer's death. Dewing writes, "I am very sorry to hear that you are laid up. Gerald and Alma were here yesterday (Thayer's son and daughter-in-law) bringing a portrait of your Mary, done perhaps thirty years ago . . . . It is superb, one of your most important things."[1] A more complete account of this episode was presented in an article by Dewing's wife:

> And just a week before his death, his son brought for us to see a portrait head of his daughter Mary at the age of eighteen, a head that had been found this winter hidden in some corner all these years. It is one of Thayer's greatest masterpieces — a head as good as Rembrandt. He had been dissatisfied with the value of the dark background and very characteristicly he had painted a narrow stripe of light blue on either side, apparently quite unrelated to the design, and yet the savant might see that these stripes should not be removed. The value was perfect, they helped the head — the beautiful head — what matter to Thayer was anything else?[2]

Mary was born while Thayer was a student of art in Paris, March 11, 1876. If, as Mrs. Dewing says, she was eighteen when the Hyde portrait was painted, the date for the work should be 1894, and not the 1902 as generally given. Since 1902 does appear in early publications, perhaps it refers to the time the curious stripes were added by the artist, which finally completed the composition to his satisfaction.

Abbott Thayer, like Eakins before him, studied in Paris with the painter Jean Léon Gérôme. Thayer appears to have reacted against Gérôme's style in the same way that Eakins did, preferring large simple figures painted with visible brushwork in relatively somber tones to Gérôme's smooth surfaces, complicated compositions, and bright palette.

At the close of the last century Abbott Thayer was universally recognized to be one of America's most important living artists. His art had two subjects only, the ideal female form and landscape. His fame rested on his image of women. Like his friend and contemporary the sculptor Daniel Chester French, he found in living models the ideal that he sought. More often than not it is the faces of his friends and family that are portrayed; Mary herself served as the model in a number of his allegorical works.[3]

1. Thomas Dewing, *The Arts,* Thayer Memorial Number, June-July, 1921, p. 24.
2. Maria Oakey Dewing, "Abbott Thayer — a Portrait and an Appreciation," *The International Studio,* LXXIV, August, 1921, p. XIV and frontispiece, p. (7).
3. In 1906 Mary was married to an English naturalist, Fred Birch.

Provenance: The first owner was the collector of Thayer's work, John Gellatly, who appears to have been a family friend, and to have specifically collected paintings by Thayer in which Thayer's family appears. The above cited documents indicate it was in the possession of the Thayer family at his death, May 21, 1921; purchased through E. and A. Milch, Inc., New York, April 1922, from the Thayer Memorial Exhibition.

Literature: Thomas Dewing, *op. cit.;* Mary Oakey Dewing, *op. cit.;* Metropolitan Museum of Art, *Memorial Exhibition of the Works of Abbott Handerson Thayer,* New York, March 20-April 30, 1922, p. 10, no. 56; Nathaniel Pousette-Dart, and Royal Cortissoz, *Abbott H. Thayer,* 1923, illustrated, p. (31); Nelson C. White, *Abbott H. Thayer,* Hartford, 1951, pl. XXI.

Exhibitions: Metropolitan Museum of Art, New York, March 20-April 30, 1922.

108. Albert Pinkham Ryder

American, 1847-1917

Stag in the Forest of Arden (Formerly *The Centaur.*) c. 1897

Oil on canvas. 30.6 x 30.6 cm. (12-1/16 x 12-1/16") 1971.43

This composition is closely related to that of two other paintings by Ryder, *The Forest of Arden,* 1897, in the collection of Stephen C. Clark, Cooperstown,[1] and *Diana's Hunt,* listed as part of the collection of Mr. Ralph Cudney, Chicago.[2] The creature identified as a centaur in the Hyde painting seems to be more clearly a deer, perhaps in flight. (The equally obscure forms in the foreground of *Diana's Hunt* have been interpreted as deer.) In the three related paintings a great tree trunk with two branching arms stands at the left, while farther back on the right, trees are massed; just before the tree, water glistens.

The Forest of Arden appears in Shakespeare's *As You Like It,* Act II, Scene I. There a reference is made to a stag hunt, which could be the true subject of the *Diana's Hunt,* and the so-called centaur figure in the Hyde work appears to be a running stag. The centaur is a creature from Greek mythology. Classical themes are quite rare in Ryder's art. His subject sources are usually those of romantic artists elsewhere, coming from medieval and late medieval times.

A romantic in every sense, Ryder was devoted to nature, but curiously found all the landscape he required in the parks around New York. From a letter it is known that the Bronx Park was his inspiration for the *Forest of Arden.* However, Ryder never transcribed the topography of a specific place. It was always a generalized mood that he sought, of landscape scenes in moonlight, or in the low light of the sun. He never made drawings, but rather his forms came directly from his imagination. In the studio his compositions evolved over extended periods of time as the artist searched for the most potent and mood-provoking forms. In the way of romantics, emotional expression was more important to Ryder than was meaning or beauty, and with the true romantic's disdain for the restrictions imposed by proper techniques and procedures, his forms were never very naturalistic. Moreover, his paintings were so poor technically that they began to deteriorate almost from the day they were completed. The Hyde painting has become partly illegible by a darkening of the surface and by the dramatic pulling apart of the paint, the result of Ryder's placing fresh layers of paint and varnish over paint that had not sufficiently dried.

1. Lloyd Goodrich, *Albert P. Ryder,* New York, 1959, p. 28. The *Forest of Arden* in the Clark Collection is illustrated, pl. 77 and 78.
2. Frederick Price Newlin, *Ryder: A Study of Appreciation,* New York, 1932, no. 32.

Provenance: Percy Kitchell, Providence, Rhode Island; Mrs. Cornelius J. Sullivan, purchased from William Macbeth, Inc., 1935.

Literature: Charles C. Eldredge, *American Imagination and Symbolist Painting,* Helen Foresman Spencer Museum of Art, University of Kansas, Lawrence, 1979, no. 53, p. 163, illustrated no. 5, p. 35.

Exhibitions: The Grey Art Gallery and Study Center, New York University, October 24-December 28, 1979; Helen Foresman Spencer Museum of Art, The University of Kansas, January 20-March 2, 1980.

109. Anna Hyatt Huntington

American, 1876-1973

Mountain Lion, c. 1915

Bronze. 17.1 x 11.4 x 5.4 cm. (6-3/4 x 4-1/2 x 2-1/8″) 1971.96
Signed back of sculpture at base: "Anna V. Hyatt"
Inscribed on base: "45 GORHAM CO. FOUNDERS 0.88."

This sculpture portrays a mountain lion crawling over a rock with its body pressed to the surface as if it were cautiously approaching a prey. The work closely resembles the small animal sculptures of the French artist Antoine Louis Barye (1796-1875). As in Barye's style the form is extremely naturalistic, and is rendered as a compact mass, fused to the rock over which it climbs.

In the first quarter of the twentieth century Anna Hyatt Huntington had achieved international fame for her equestrian monuments. In America her most famous work is a statue of Joan of Arc in Central Park, New York City. In 1912 she received the curious distinction of being one of twelve American women to achieve an annual income of over $50,000. Among the honors she received for her work were the Rodin Gold Medal, Philadelphia, 1917; the Chevalier of the Legion of Honor in France in 1922; and in Seville, the Royal Cross for her statue of El Cid.

In 1923 she married Archer Milton Huntington, heir to the Huntington shipping and railroad fortune. She and her husband in 1930 set up Brookgreen Gardens in South Carolina near Myrtle Beach. A 16,000 acre estate now open to the public, it serves both as a wildlife preserve and as a setting for the work of the artist and of the sculptors of her generation.

110. George Wesley Bellows

American, 1882-1925

Portrait of Mary Brown Tyler ?, c. 1919

Oil on canvas. 76.5 x 63.5 cm. (30-1/8 x 25″) 1971.8
Signed lower left: "George Bellows."
Gift of Hirschl and Adler Galleries, Inc., New York.

The sitter may be identified because of the similarity of her facial features to Bellows' portrait of Mary Brown Tyler, *Mrs. T. in Cream Silk* (Hirschhorn Museum and Sculpture Gardens, Washington, D.C.). Bellows met Mary Tyler at a party while he was in Chicago teaching at The Art Institute in 1919. He asked her to pose for him. Most, if not all, of Bellows' portraits were uncommissioned and were executed by the artist solely as personal artistic expressions. In choosing to portray the face of an old woman, Bellows allied himself with the realistic portrait style of his American predecessor Thomas Eakins, and further back in time, to the portraits of Rembrandt.

In 1904 Bellows was a student of the painter Robert Henri at William Merritt Chase's New York School of Art. It was possibly due to Henri's influence that Bellows' art, like Henri's, consisted primarily of close views of unidealized human forms. With Henri he was associated with the Ash Can school of New York artists, so-called because of their penchant for subjects taken from the ordinary world.

Besides portraits, Bellows also executed many landscapes. It is curious then that he is best known for his few paintings of prize-fighters.

Provenance: H. V. Allison and Company, Inc., New York; Hirschl and Adler Galleries, Inc., New York, 1969.

111. Yasuo Kuniyoshi

Japanese/American, 1893-1953

A Friend, c. 1940

Oil on canvas. 41 x 30.6 cm. (16-1/8 x 12-1/16″) 1971.26
Signed lower right: "Kuniyoshi."

For some time the name of Helena Rubenstein of cosmetics fame has been associated with this portrait. No documents support this identification, nor does it appear possible, for all Helena Rubenstein's talents at self-preservation, that this could be a portrait of a woman in her 69th year. The 1940 date of the work seems to be correct. Not only is it consistent with Kuniyoshi's style of the time, but a drawing study for this painting, dated 1940, was for sale in 1969 at M. Knoedler and Co., Inc., New York.

Kuniyoshi is the only American artist of his period (1920's-30's) who is represented in The Hyde Collection. His art belongs with a specific tendency in the American art of the time that formed an artistic mean between the extremes of modernism and the social realism of Robert Henri and the Ash Can school.

Yasuo Kuniyoshi was born in Japan, but his education in art was acquired entirely in this country at the Los Angeles School of Art and Design and in New York at the National Academy of Design and at the Art Students League. Kuniyoshi and others claim that his art is a reconciliation of the Orient and the Occident; this is not clearly borne out in his style. European modernism seems to have provided Kuniyoshi with his antecedents. In the first phase of his evolution, the art of Marc Chagall seems to have been Kuniyoshi's source. Like Chagall, his paintings present consciously naive fantasies hung on a pseudo-Cubist structure. The Hyde portrait belongs to the second phase of his career, which occurred after a visit to Paris in the 1920's. Kuniyoshi, probably influenced by Jules Pascin, abandoned fantasy and devoted himself to what could be called studio subjects: nudes, still lifes, and portraits. In this he can be identified with an entire school of American painters devoted to these traditional studio subjects, most of whom were his friends; such artists as Bernard Karfiol and Alexander Brook. In the summers they gathered at Woodstock, New York, and Ogunquit, Maine.

During the thirties Kuniyoshi's palette developed the curious monochrome of grays and browns which are present in this portrait. Quite seriously he explored the effect of nuances of value, almost as the Cubists had done in their analytical phase. But his concern appears to have been more expressive than formal.

Provenance: The artist; Edith Halpert's Downtown Gallery, New York; purchased, 1945.

112. Dorothy Dehner

American

Low Landscape Sideways, 1962

Solid cast bronze. 45.7 x 121.9 x 15.2 cm. (18 x 48 x 6″) 1971.93
Signed and dated lower left: "Dehner 62"; Inscribed center, inverted: "I love David" (?).
Purchased by funds donated by the friends of Jeanne Wilmarth Hallenback in her memory.

The title of this sculpture was given by the artist, probably at the same time she made the decision to display it upright. The original intention may have been to present it lying flat as were the other landscape sculptures executed by Dorothy Dehner early in the 1960's. The style classifies the work with modern abstract formalism. It is a pure and ordered design in the Cubist tradition. As is the case with Picasso's Cubist paintings, the form is broken into many small fragments, arranged in a rectilinear order. Characteristic of Cubism is the way the artist has set up a continual interchange between solid and void within a very shallow space. With the suggested representational content of a landscape the work is reminiscent of the landscapes of the Swiss artist Paul Klee who had a similar evolutionary association with Cubism.

Dorothy Dehner was married to the American sculptor David Smith (1906-1965) from 1927 to c. 1952. They met while both were students at the Art Students League in New York. While her work was naturally influenced by Smith's, his style is much more closely imitated by many contemporary sculptors in welded steel. Dehner's choice of cast bronze as a medium immediately sets a distance between her work and Smith's later style. Her forms are generally smaller in scale (like Smith's early work) and they are less monumental in effect.

In fact, David Smith's later work may show Dehner's influence. The sculpture *Beka* (Metropolitan Museum of Art, New York) and its companion-piece, untitled, still in the family collection at Bolton Landing, New York, both show an arrangement of rectilinear forms in a two-dimensional plane reminiscent of Dehner's sculptures of two or three years earlier.

Provenance: Purchased from the Willard Galleries, New York, January 22, 1968.

Exhibitions: The Hyde Collection, May 21-June 18, 1967.

Designed by: William Padgett, Syracuse, New York
Photography: black and white, Joseph Levy, Saratoga Springs, New York
                color, Courtney Frisse, Syracuse, New York
Printed by: Whitman Press, Lebanon, New Hampshire
Paper: Finch Opaque (neutral pH), Smooth Finish, basis 80, Bright White
Typesetting: Data Scan Typesetting, Inc., Syracuse, New York